*You
Simply Can't
Spoil a*
Newborn

You Simply Can't Spoil a Newborn

The essential Kiwi guide to nurturing
your baby in the first three months

Dorothy Waide

with Jill Daamen

David Bateman

Text © Dorothy Waide and Jill Daamen
Typography and design © David Bateman Ltd, 2015

Published in 2015 by David Bateman Ltd
30 Tarndale Grove, Albany, Auckland, New Zealand
Reprinted 2016

www.batemanpublishing.co.nz

ISBN 978-1-86953-892-7

Publisher: Bill Honeybone
Designer: Carolyn Lewis
Cover image by Sam Mothersole Photography; back cover image of author by Fiona Tomlinson.
Internal images courtesy of Jane Anne McAllister, Dimples by Jane Anne (pages 2, 8, 67, 109, 131, 175, 205 and 214–5); Sam Mothersole Photography (pages 12–13, 17, 44–5, 51, 53–56, 59, 61, 63, 70, 75, 77, 82–3, 87, 93, 96, 99–103, 106, 112–13, 115, 129, 147–8, 156, 160–65, 184–5 and 191); Keri-Anne Dilworth, First Light Birth Photography (pages 6–7, 10, 19, 23–4, 26, 35, 37–8, 40–41, 90–91, 105 and 120); shutterstock.com (pages 48, 64, 144–5, 151, 152–3, 170, 172–3, 179, 196, 206–207 and 208). Sketches courtesy of istock by Getty Images, istockphoto.com.

Printed in China through Colorcraft Ltd, Hong Kong

*For all the babies, mums and dads in the world
who have taught me all I know.
Every day I learn something new from you all,
and the day I stop learning is the day I retire.*

Contents

Foreword

There's no way to define or articulate the joys of parenthood — it's just a gorgeous, wonderful feeling of unequivocal love. With children there is no judgment, both in your love for them and in their love for you.

Dorothy first joined us as a baby nurse following the birth of our son, and again a few years later when our daughter was born.

Dorothy's knowledge of babies and small children is phenomenal, and firmly rooted in years of working with babies and parents. A gifted and talented professional, she is a tower of strength, tireless in her energy and commitment. We can honestly say we never found a baby-related problem that Dorothy was unable to solve.

Her enormous sense of warmth, love and a down-to-earth philosophy always made us feel safe in our role as parents.

Dorothy's approach is never generic — her tenet is that every baby and every parent is different.

Each situation is treated with the utmost care and consideration, with wonderful tact and a sense of humour, guiding our children — and us as parents — through each stage of development.

One of her many remarkable skills is an ability to teach babies how to self-settle and resettle so that they sleep soundly through the night, a valuable gift that she gave both our children. By providing a structured, yet nurturing and flexible environment based on the needs of the baby, there was no need for difficult routines or too many sleepless nights.

You Simply Can't Spoil a Newborn brings together Dorothy's three decades of expertise; it is smart, reassuring and to the point — a must-have for new parents everywhere.

Catherine Zeta-Jones and Michael Douglas

About Dorothy Waide
Baby Guru to the Stars

Dorothy Waide is one of the world's most sought-after baby consultants, celebrated for her practical approach to baby care, practised over a career spanning three decades. After training as a Karitane Mothercraft nurse in New Zealand in the 1970s, Dorothy spent more than 20 years overseas sharing the homes of Hollywood celebrities, media magnates and leading business people, who required nothing but the best. Typically, she would spend two weeks to six months with the family of a new baby, guiding and supporting them on their journey as parents.

Dubbed 'The Baby Guru', 'Mary Poppins', or 'The Baby Whisperer', Dorothy is the first to point out that her role is not about being bedazzled by the big names and gorgeous homes or jetting around the world — it's about welcoming a new life.

On her arrival at a new job, Dorothy would quickly adjust to the family's daily rhythm. By the end of her stay, she would leave behind more self-assured and relaxed parents, confident to continue their journey forward.

Her expertise crosses cultural and geographical boundaries — she has worked in Europe, Asia, Australia, New Zealand, the United Kingdom and the United States. Her uncanny ability to calm even the most fractious baby or toddler, combined with her depth of knowledge, sets Dorothy apart as one of today's most respected baby consultants.

According to the many satisfied clients across the globe whose lives she has touched, 'what Dorothy doesn't know about babies is not worth knowing'.

PART ONE
Setting the Scene

Why Nurturing Matters

Think of it from your newborn baby's perspective: nine months of being protected and cushioned by amniotic fluid with muted light, the hypnotic sound of your heartbeat, food on tap, no schedule to adhere to ...

And then birth.

To a newborn, our world looms brightly lit, noisy and unfamiliar. In response to this stimulation, your baby's senses register on high alert. Every moment is a new experience.

Nature equips your newborn with vital reflexes — among them the startle reflex (the Moro reflex), the ability to grasp, the rooting reflex — plus an instinct for survival. To grow and develop, babies need food and sleep. To thrive, they need nurturing, love and security.

Spoiling doesn't come into it — it's impossible to shower your baby with too much love!

My decision to focus on the first three months of parenthood is a simple one: this extraordinary newborn phase offers a unique opportunity for parents to lay a loving and solid foundation that will last a lifetime.

It is also when parents — whether first-time or not — need unfailing support to help them deal with the countless decisions they face every day. Questions such as:

*These early weeks are an ideal opportunity
to hibernate at home, enjoy your baby and
get to know each other. I believe that doing
this will help lay sound foundations for
the rest of your baby's life.*

- Will rocking my baby to sleep mean I'll be rocking a toddler to sleep in a year's time?
- Can I breastfeed with mastitis?
- Should I wake my newborn to feed during the night?
- If I bottle-feed, does it make me a bad parent?

All parents want reassurance that they are on the right path, and to know that they are doing the best for their baby. No one deliberately sets out *not* to be the best parent.

I truly believe there is no right or wrong way of caring for a baby. There are easier and more difficult ways, but often what appears to be the easiest option — or 'short cut' — turns out to be the hardest in the long run.

In writing *You Simply Can't Spoil a Newborn*, my aim is to help parents avoid the pitfalls common in the first 12 weeks. It is not a 'rule book', but collates tried-and-tested methods that are easily implemented into daily life. Reassuring without being prescriptive, it takes into account modern lifestyles and recognises that every baby — and every parent — is different.

My aim is to provide you with choices so you can find your own path according to what will work best in your family and household.

From calming the most unsettled baby to teaching babies to self-settle and resettle, I offer realistic advice on how to solve common breastfeeding issues and to manage time, relationships and emotional demands in the weeks following birth.

While many of today's parenting books are written by psychologists, paediatricians and academics, *You Simply Can't Spoil a Newborn* is based on round-the-clock, hands-on experience gleaned over three decades while working in homes across the world, supporting parents from different cultural and economic backgrounds.

'Leave Well Alone'
Happy baby, happy mummy. Don't change anything! Changes are only necessary if you or your baby is unhappy, or if what you are doing is no longer working — at the end of the day if nothing is wrong, leave well alone.

Babies the world over need unconditional love, consistency and boundaries to help them make sense of their new world and their place in it. I believe nurturing is the secret to cushioning your baby's transition from womb to world, encouraging them to feed and sleep well.

In my experience, rigid routines place unnecessary pressure on parents and lead to clock-watching; and the result is parents forgetting to enjoy their baby. Likewise, attachment parenting that is exclusively baby-led can be strenuous, physically and emotionally demanding, and difficult to sustain. My approach blends parent-led and baby-led parenting — I take the best from both worlds and go straight down the middle.

With this in mind, I believe the best routine is one that fits with your family, reflects the needs of you and your baby, and naturally evolves out of your baby's sleeping and feeding rhythms. Where necessary I help parents create a rhythm that gives shape to the day without the need for unyielding schedules or excessive clock-watching.

At the heart of *You Simply Can't Spoil a Newborn* are the all-important chapters on sleeping, self-settling and resettling, which outline my unique 'nurturing within arms' approach to helping newborns find sleep.

In my experience, babies under 12–16 weeks do not have the ability to settle themselves to sleep — they are not born with the skills. Therefore it is pointless (and goes against nurturing) to leave them alone in a bassinet or cot to cry/grizzle — they have no idea how to fall sleep and need us as 'teachers' to intervene and guide them.

While self-settling and resettling cannot be taught overnight, the first 12 weeks offer a perfect opportunity to begin building the foundations so that

somewhere between 12 and 16 weeks, they will have the fundamental skills — and confidence — to be able to self-settle and resettle on their own with little intervention.

Recognising the all-important connection between feeding and sleeping, I highlight to parents the repercussions of waking a baby for a 'dream feed', feeding a baby to sleep, catnapping, and 'snacking'.

This book is written for fatigued parents with little time on their hands, so I've kept the details clear and succinct, using bullet points, photographs and illustrations for quick reference. It is structured by topic rather than developmental stages, acknowledging that babies grow at different rates.

Parenting is about discovering what is best for you and your baby. I encourage you to tune in to your baby's needs and follow your instincts to interpret when your baby is tired, hungry or wants cuddles. In doing so you will help build your baby's trust in their new world and boost your confidence as a loving and attentive parent.

Whether you are living in a Hollywood mansion or on a remote farm in rural New Zealand, my core message to all parents is simple: *you simply can't spoil a newborn.* It is impossible to shower your baby with too much love.

Focus on You

Early parenting is extremely physical and emotionally draining. Yet your well-being is just as important to your baby's growth and development now as it was during your pregnancy. The happier and healthier you are, the better prepared you'll be to care for both yourself and your newborn in the coming weeks.

- Look after yourself. Get extra rest.
- Worry less about doing things the 'right' way.
- Ask for and accept offers of help.
- Pay attention to your feelings.
- Rest when your baby rests; eat when your baby eats.

Be kind to yourself. Both you and your newborn will need extra rest and this will be so much easier if you have an extra set of hands. Whether from a qualified person, a close friend or a family member, ask for and accept help so you can build up reserves. You don't have to do it all on your own.

However, if you are without help, try to rest when your baby sleeps. Resist falling into the trap of 'I'll just do the washing/mop the floors, etc.' and then have a lie down — in the first few weeks there is no guarantee how long your baby will sleep. Rest first, chores second. A mini-nap can do wonders to replenish energy.

Keep snacks and water on hand so that when your baby feeds, you can refuel too. If you also have a toddler or two, napping together in the afternoon is a calming way for the family to bond and share time.

For some mothers, postnatal hormones create a sense of euphoria and a surge of energy that can suddenly and dramatically subside in the first week. Being aware of this can help you manage your time and energy better, and confirms that what you are going through is normal.

Have No Expectations

Don't worry about doing things the 'right' way. Practise trial and error, and don't expect perfection from yourself or your baby. Try not to feel guilty if sometimes you get it wrong or *think* you have got it wrong — remember there is no right or wrong way to parent. Besides, babies are endlessly forgiving! The fewer expectations you place on yourself — and your baby — the better your experience will be.

Pay attention to your feelings. It is natural to experience extreme emotion and mixed feelings in the early weeks in response to hormonal changes, lack of sleep and the sheer emotional impact of being a new parent. Many mothers talk about the overwhelming love they feel for their baby, but fewer speak openly about the feelings of inadequacy, anxiety and misgivings that they experience while facing their new responsibilities. It's far more common than you imagine. Feeling apprehensive does not make you a bad mother! Most mothers take time to find their feet.

Some don't know what to share with partners, family or friends and what not to share. They worry that sharing too much may reveal incompetence or vulnerability. Yet not sharing can be overwhelming.

Unburdening your feelings can help lighten the load. If you have a partner, involving them gives them an opportunity to understand what you are going through and, more often than not, helps strengthen your bond. As time passes, the more confident you will both become — and the easier it will get.

Staying Positive
- Take your time.
- As much as possible, stay calm and be patient.
- Surround yourself with good friends and supportive family members.
- Ask for help, don't wait for offers.
- Don't feel you need to present yourself as a 'perfect mother' — she doesn't exist!
- There's no such thing as a perfect baby either.
- Don't feel beholden to arrangements — it's okay to say no.
- Cut yourself some slack.

Time Management

What doesn't get done today can always wait until tomorrow.

The biggest change will be the pace at which you live — everything now takes longer than you expect. Gone are the days when just hopping in the car and driving to the shops takes 20 minutes — it will take you all that time just to get into the car!

A good idea is to do as much as you can in the morning when you have more energy, so that the afternoon is available for you to be with your baby — or deal with the unexpected.

Try not to be over-ambitious. Mothers often comment that they haven't achieved much in a day. Wonderful! To me, that's a sign of good parenting and that your priorities are right. All this goes a long way in giving your baby a sense of security so that they feel considered and their needs met.

Don't feel beholden to arrangements. I believe it is always a new mother's prerogative to change her mind.

Be Assertive with Visitors

Managing your social environment is a sure-fire way to conserve energy. If visitors arrive at naptime, you are not obliged to meet your usual standards of hospitality. Be assertive and create space for yourselves. Try not to over-commit. In these early weeks it is more important to be respectful to your own, your baby's and your immediate family's needs, than to accommodate others.

A good suggestion is to make a simple sign to put on your front door that reads: *Thanks for dropping by. Sorry — we are currently sleeping. Please email/ text and let's arrange a time for you to come and have cuddles with the baby.* This also prevents couriers and salespeople from banging down your door.

Time Out

Moments of utter exhaustion, insecurity or despair are more common than you think yet many mothers don't talk openly about them for fear of seeming a failure. *Parenting isn't about achievement — it's not a competition!*

Showing your emotions, being upset and feeling worn out are all relevant in building your relationship with your newborn and finding your way together.

It is only natural that you want to be the best you can be with your baby, but it is also okay to admit that when your baby is crying and inconsolable, you might not feel in a loving or nurturing mood. Bonding isn't just about the good times and the cuddles — it's also about navigating your way through the tough times. Take heart ... and a deep breath. In these situations, give yourself some distance from your baby. Call someone. Ask for help. Make someone listen to you. Have the confidence to stand back and hand the reins to someone you trust when you most need to.

It is not a failure to ask for help — on the contrary, it demonstrates that you know your limits and are able to respect them.

When making decisions:
- be consistent, think it through and follow it through
- always work within your limits and not those of others
- it's about matching your needs and your baby's needs
- assess your challenges with an open and objective mind
- when you get things wrong, don't be too hard on yourself — mistakes help us learn.

Supporting Your Partner in Their New Role

22

Your partner can be your greatest ally. That said there might be occasions when they question your parenting to the point of appearing critical.

Remind yourself that he or she is learning along the way and that this is new territory for both of you. It is inevitable that you are both feeling sensitive, insecure and, as a result, are judging yourself and each other, both of you anxious and desperate to do the right thing and fearful of failure. Tempers may be frayed, wires crossed and communication may suffer or become unclear.

Most partners want to be involved but feel they simply don't know how to help. To them, it may seem you are constantly occupied with parenting tasks that cannot be outsourced so easily.

From the outset, find ways that your partner can be actively involved and gently encourage them to do so. For example, partners make great 'human beds' and can be useful to help soothe your baby to sleep.

Here's how to do it. After feeding, pass your baby to your partner, who will immediately draw confidence in knowing that their baby will not need to be fed again for at least the next hour and a half. This empowers them to cope confidently when your baby cries, immediately being able to rule out hunger in favour of tiredness. This works especially well for partners of mothers who are breastfeeding — they often feel redundant.

Other partner-friendly tasks include burping, bathing your baby, nappy changing and bottle-feeding. Preparing meals, making the bed and organising other household chores that you have not been able to get to are also ways your partner can support you.

Take care not to bombard your partner with instructions or undermine them. A good way to get the ball rolling is to demonstrate how you do a certain activity, gently suggesting, 'Here's an easy way that seems to work.' *Then leave them to it.* I can't stress this enough.

Giving your partner space and trust is important. It is so easy for a protective mother to feel they need to micro-manage every task but, more often than not, your partner will do an exceptional job, and trusting them to do so will not only boost their confidence but will help you both psychologically and physically. Most mothers are relieved to have an ally, but some need to learn how to 'let go' a little.

Alternatively, you may be able to convince your partner that a shoulder or foot rub is a valuable contribution to shared or holistic parenting. It's worth a try!

Try to work as a team. Above all, be kind to each other and make an extra effort not to criticise, especially when tempers seem set to flare.

Dealing with Outside Influences

Parents and In-laws

- Set the ground rules at the outset, ideally together.
- Tell them how you value their support and politely give them pointers on how they can help out.
- Keep in mind that parenting styles change from generation to generation and at times you may disagree with each other's methods.
- Try to remember that, on the whole, most family members are well meaning in their intentions.

25

Bossy Friends and Other Vocal People
Listen, filter, agree to disagree …

It is likely you will get advice from everyone who walks through your door. Whether you intend to breastfeed, choose cloth nappies or disposable, or plan to return to work or stay at home, people around you may feel compelled to decide for you, or at least comment. This is your chance to lay the foundations for how you wish to parent, based on your own needs and no one else's. It doesn't cost to listen, but it is up to you as to what you take on board.

Media and Social Media
Information is readily available these days from a variety of sources. Think about the purpose of the publication and the 'expert' being interviewed — is it genuine information, or marketing or political propaganda? What are their qualifications? How experienced are they? Most importantly, does what they claim resonate with you and how you wish to parent? This also goes for baby experts both in the non-medical and medical fields. It is important that parents remain confident and follow their instincts when seeking advice. In my experience, a mother and father's intuition can be a valuable tool. If you feel uneasy about advice you are given, weigh it up, follow your gut and get a second opinion.

26

> By 10 days or two weeks, your baby will begin
> to feel more at ease in their new world and,
> like a rosebud, will slowly begin to unfurl,
> gradually feeling more confident.

While blogs, tweets, forums and social media offer a platform for parents to share common interests, keep in mind that this is unedited information provided through the filter of the writer. Try not to be overly swayed. Let your common sense prevail.

Resist comparing your situation with those of celebrities publicised in the media — more often than not it is the glossy, sanitised version and not the full story. Believe me, I know!

Extended Family

There may be family expectations involving traditions or cultural norms, or maybe you find yourself confronted with dominant family characters eager to have a say. At the end of the day, no one can argue the fact that it's your turn to parent.

Adopt an 'It's Okay' Mantra

It's okay:

- if the house is a mess
- to be in your PJs at 3 p.m. — or all day
- to stipulate visiting times
- to turn away visitors if you're not up to it
- to refuse to wake your sleeping baby just so visitors can have a peek
- to ask house guests to wait on you, rather than the other way around
- to request visitors to wash their hands or use hand gel before holding your baby.

Baby Blues and Postnatal Depression

Hormones in the First Few Days

Most mothers experience a range of emotions in the first few days, often intensified by the hormone fluctuations that follow birth. This is all quite normal, especially around day three or four when mothers typically feel weepy, overwhelmed or irritable for a few hours, or even days. These 'baby blues' often coincide with the milk coming in and pregnancy hormones subsiding.

Postnatal Depression

Postnatal depression (PND) is a treatable illness of varying degrees that is more common than most people realise. It is thought to affect 10 to 15 per cent of mothers, although studies suggest that PND is often misdiagnosed or unreported, and that the actual figure could be as high as 25 or 30 per cent.

It's important to know that while some mothers develop PND in the first six weeks following childbirth, it can occur at any time throughout the first year.

If you think that you may have PND, it is vital you contact your GP, midwife or health visitor, who will be able to help you find the best treatment. Support to help you manage the condition includes counselling and medication. My advice is to seek help sooner rather than later — and stay strong in knowing there is no shame in asking for support.

Often it's a close friend, family member or partner who recognises the warning signs, which is why it's a good idea that everyone is informed of what symptoms to watch for.

Symptoms of PND can include some or all of the following:

- low mood
- constant exhaustion
- feelings of guilt
- difficulty sleeping
- difficulties bonding with your baby
- low energy
- crying for no reason
- sadness
- inability to cope
- overwhelming anxiety
- lack of appetite or a sugar buzz
- relationship difficulties with your partner
- social withdrawal from family and friends.

See the Edinburgh Postnatal Depression Scale (EPDS) on pages 29–31.

Edinburgh Postnatal Depression Scale (EPDS)

As you are pregnant or have recently had a baby, we would like to know how you are feeling.

Please choose the answer that comes closest to how you have felt in the past 7 days, not just how you feel today.

In the past 7 days:

1. I have been able to laugh and see the funny side of things
   - ☐ As much as I always could
   - ☐ Not quite so much now
   - ☐ Definitely not so much now
   - ☐ Not at all

2. I have looked forward with enjoyment to things
   - ☐ As much as I ever did
   - ☐ Rather less than I used to
   - ☐ Definitely less than I used to
   - ☐ Hardly at all

*3. I have blamed myself unnecessarily when things went wrong
   - ☐ Yes, most of the time
   - ☐ Yes, some of the time
   - ☐ Not very often
   - ☐ No, never

4. I have been anxious or worried for no good reason
   - ☐ No, not at all
   - ☐ Hardly ever
   - ☐ Yes, sometimes
   - ☐ Yes, very often

*5. I have felt scared or panicky for no very good reason
   - ☐ Yes, quite a lot
   - ☐ Yes, sometimes
   - ☐ No, not much
   - ☐ No, not at all

*6. Things have been getting on top of me
☐ Yes, most of the time, I haven't been able to cope at all
☐ Yes, sometimes I haven't been coping as well as usual
☐ No, most of the time I have coped quite well
☐ No, I have been coping as well as ever

*7. I have been so unhappy that I have had difficulty sleeping
☐ Yes, most of the time
☐ Yes, sometimes
☐ Not very often
☐ No, not at all

*8. I have felt sad or miserable
☐ Yes, most of the time
☐ Yes, quite often
☐ Not very often
☐ No, not at all

*9. I have been so unhappy that I have been crying
☐ Yes, most of the time
☐ Yes, quite often
☐ Only occasionally
☐ No, never

*10. The thought of harming myself has occurred to me
☐ Yes, quite often
☐ Sometimes
☐ Hardly ever
☐ Never

Postpartum depression is the most common complication of childbearing. The 10-question Edinburgh Postnatal Depression Scale (EPDS) is a valuable and efficient way of identifying patients at risk for 'perinatal' depression. The EPDS is easy to administer and has proven to be an effective screening tool.

Mothers who score above 13 are likely to be suffering from a depressive illness of varying severity. The EPDS score should not override clinical judgment. A careful clinical assessment should be carried out to confirm the diagnosis. The scale indicates how the mother has felt during the previous week. In doubtful cases it may be useful to repeat the tool after 2 weeks. The scale will not detect mothers with anxiety neuroses, phobias or personality disorders.

SCORING

Questions 1, 2 and 4 (without an *) are scored 0, 1, 2 or 3 with top box scored as 0 and the bottom box scored as 3.
Questions 3, 5–10 (marked with an *) are reverse scored, with the top box scored as 3 and the bottom box scored as 0.

Maximum score: 30
Possible depression: 10 or greater
Always look at Question 10 (suicidal thoughts)

Instructions for using the Edinburgh Postnatal Depression Scale:
1. The mother is asked to check the response that comes closest to how she has been feeling in the previous 7 days.
2. All items must be completed.
3. Care should be taken to avoid the possibility of the mother discussing her answers with others (answers come from the mother or pregnant woman).
4. The mother should complete the scale herself, unless she has limited English or has difficulty with reading.

Postnatal Psychosis

Postnatal psychosis is a serious condition thought to affect one or two women in every 1000 post-birth. The causes are not fully understood, although hormonal and biological imbalances are thought to be contributing factors.

Postnatal psychosis commonly occurs in the first few weeks and is characterised by symptoms of psychosis, including some or all of the following:

- feeling out of touch with reality
- hallucinations and delusions
- confused or disturbed thoughts
- mania or hyperactivity
- loss of appetite or excessive eating
- feelings of suicide
- thoughts of harming yourself or the baby
- trouble sleeping
- severe depression.

Sufferers are often unaware of their behaviour. Therefore it is crucial that partners, friends and family remain vigilant for signs and contact a health professional immediately if they suspect postnatal psychosis. A case in Invercargill in late 2013 highlighted the near-tragic outcome of not identifying a mother's condition. Fortunately, the family has been reunited.

Dads and Postnatal Depression

Fathers also suffer from PND, but this is not often talked about. It is not uncommon for fathers to experience irritability, anxiety, sleeping difficulties, a loss of humour or a tendency to withdraw from people, adding to stress levels at work and creating tension in the relationship. Contact your health professional — it's important to realise that there's no need to suffer in silence and there is help at hand.

Several studies have linked the pressure to be a good parent or 'super mum' and 'super dad' to the exacerbation of mental illness. Both mothers and fathers need to pay attention to their mental health during the perinatal period — the weeks before, during and after birth.

Words of Wisdom
'It's my third baby — I should know!'
No, not necessarily ... every baby is different.
Parenting is bespoke: there isn't a one-size-
fits-all template for bringing up a baby.

Tips for Stitches and Bits

If you've had stitches, your bits feel bruised or tender, and it hurts when you wee, use a water bottle to spray or pour water over the area while passing urine. When drying, use a hair dryer set on low heat, rather than a towel. Wearing a frozen sanitary pad, or a disposable glove with water in it, gives temporary relief. Caesarean section wounds can be kept dry and protected by placing a maternity pad between the wound and your knickers.

Becoming Pregnant Again

Contrary to what many mothers are told or believe, breastfeeding, even exclusively, will not prevent you from conceiving. Some women become fertile soon after giving birth, although more often than not they are unaware that they have ovulated.

   Check with your doctor or midwife regarding when to resume normal sexual activities and how soon to use contraception.

33

Nurture, Nurture, Nurture

The first 12 weeks — often referred to as the 'fourth trimester' — offer a perfect opportunity to *nurture our babies within arms.*

Nurturing is fundamental in helping your baby adapt to life outside the womb. It is the common thread that runs through every aspect of caring for your baby. Nurturing begins from day one and continues to evolve as your baby grows, bonds deepen and emotional needs change.

Nurturing:
- creates an environment in which your baby feels safe and learns to trust
- helps cushion your baby's transition from womb to world and forms the basis of your baby's emotional life
- offers unconditional love
- sets the tone for daily life and is the key to easing your baby into healthy sleeping and feeding rhythms.

Babies thrive on being held close and sensing the rhythm of your heartbeat, your familiar smell and the warmth of your body. This intimacy emulates the womb and helps build a sense of trust, confirming to your baby that life outside the womb is safe.

In a sense, parents are like shock absorbers — holding your baby close absorbs their anxiety and tension so they are able to relax and feel secure.

The more time you are able to spend with your newborn, the more confident and reassured they will feel. Like any nurturing relationship, the more at ease your baby feels, the more they will be able to relax, settle into their new world and be themselves.

Bonding deepens with time and shared experiences. As much as you can, let your newborn be the centre of your universe. If your baby cries, respond. If your baby is hungry, feed them. If the nappy needs changing, change it.

Every baby is different and some require more nurturing than others. On occasions, nurturing calls for going that extra mile to comfort your baby in times of distress. These early weeks pass so quickly and it is vital to make use of every opportunity to nurture.

Nurturing is not only about 'doing', sometimes it is simply about 'being'. Feeding, burping, changing the nappy and helping your baby find sleep are all part of nurturing and getting in tune with your baby. It does not have to be verbal and can be as passive as watching your baby while they sleep, holding them quietly in your arms, or taking an afternoon nap together.

For some parents, getting to know their baby may be the most intimate relationship they have ever experienced — and as daunting and overwhelming as it is fulfilling and rewarding. Many parents begin this journey anxious and fearful of failing. As time passes and expectations are put to rest, parents often discover an internal strength. I always encourage new parents to trust in themselves and follow their instincts — I firmly believe this is a key aspect in helping parents find their feet.

How the first weeks unfold may well be influenced by your birth experience. If your recovery from birth limits your ability to hold your baby, rest assured that just being close is beneficial for both of you.

Skin-to-skin Contact

Numerous psychological studies highlight the benefits of parents initiating skin-to-skin contact immediately after the birth and during the first few weeks. The skin-to-skin experience helps soothe a distressed baby, establishes feeding and enhances bonding.

Research published in *Biological Psychiatry* provides evidence that separating infants from their mothers for extended periods is stressful to the baby. Humans are the only mammals that practise such maternal-neonate separation and its physiological impact on the baby has been unknown until now.

Researchers measured heart rate variability in two-day-old sleeping babies for one hour each during skin-to-skin contact with mother, and alone in a bassinet/cot next to the mother's bed. Neonatal autonomic activity (disturbances of the nervous system) was 176 per cent higher and quiet sleep 86 per cent lower during maternal separation, compared with skin-to-skin contact.

There are specific things that all babies respond to, or like, and specific things they do not like.

Babies love:
- cuddles, snuggles, being engulfed in your arms
- feeding
- skin-to-skin contact
- your facial expressions
- a soothing tone of voice
- your smell
- safe co-sleeping.

Babies are stressed by:
- abrupt changes
- swift movements
- being left to cry alone for extended periods
- hunger
- not getting enough sleep — babies need to be taught how to sleep
- loud noise, bright light
- busy households
- stressed-out parents — babies sense household anxiety.

The First Few Days

So much occurs in a short space of time. How these first few days unfold may depend on your birth experience and whether or not you have other children. Cocoon yourselves and be respectful of both your need, and your baby's need, for sleep.

As much as you can, let go of outside influences and reorient your day according to your baby's pace. There will be little differentiation between night and day and much time will be spent feeding, resting and simply 'being'. This unique phase is very much about you as a family getting to know each other and being together. This intensity eases with time.

Every Baby is Unique ...

All babies are different and even those sharing the same genes can be dissimilar in many ways. Some newborns barely open their eyes in the first 10 days and may need to be woken to feed, while others are constantly alert and have difficulty sleeping.

The coming weeks are an opportunity to bond and get to know your baby.

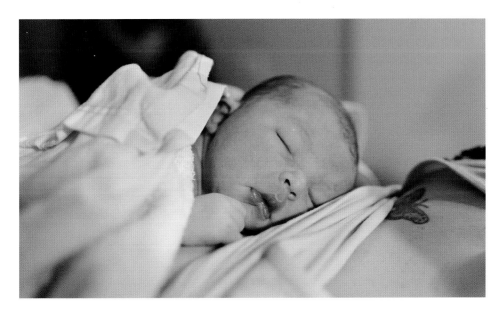

Siblings and Newborns

Pre-birth

It is important to think ahead and make any changes that involve the sibling(s) before the baby arrives. For example, if your older child needs to vacate the cot and change table, or move rooms to make space for the new baby, do so before the baby is born. This way it is less likely that the sibling will feel displaced or usurped.

Another good idea is to use children's picture books to introduce your toddler to the imminent arrival of a baby. Examples include: *Stupid Baby* by Stephanie Blake, Gecko Press; *Silly Baby* by Marie-Louise Fitzpatrick, Frances Lincoln Publishers; and *Brand New Baby* by Bob Graham, Walker Books. Check your local library or children's bookshop for other titles.

Arrange a present for the new baby to give to the sibling — ideally a doll or something related to the world of babies in a toy form. Many children see new babies as an opportunity to play at parenting. Some are content just observing. If, however, they are keen to be hands-on, try giving them a doll so they can mimic you as you prepare for, then care for your baby.

Once the Baby Arrives

Siblings can be amazingly attentive, absorbing every little detail and eager to help with their newborn sibling.

Most just want to be involved with their new brother or sister. Rather than shutting them away, which may encourage frustration or jealousy, encourage calmness as best as you can and try to answer their questions honestly. Invite them to join you during feeding, nappy changing or bathing time. Remember, it's a new and captivating experience for everyone.

Use language that connects the newborn with the sibling to help forge an early relationship and sense of belonging. Instead of talking about 'the new baby' perhaps ask 'would you like to meet your baby?' Don't assume the toddler wants to be the big girl or big boy.

As early as practicable, depending on age, include the older sibling by inviting them to cuddle the baby. This will acknowledge the toddler in their own right and make them feel loved. The best place to do this is somewhere where the parents have their hands free to support the toddler.

39

The Over-zealous Sibling

Parents need to find ways of dealing with a sibling who is showing signs of potentially hurting the baby. If you are unsure, don't be afraid to ask for help.

Toddlers respond well to positive attention — a 'catch me when I'm good' approach can prevent some negative behaviour towards the newborn.

Saying no to a toddler often has the opposite effect and only entices them to do it more. If a sibling has taken to hitting the baby, for example, it's better to make a positive intervention and prevent the hit, mid-flow, by distracting the toddler — try pointing out the window. Nine times out of ten this works.

Remember, siblings have had their world turned upside down and are still working out where everyone fits into the family dynamic. Until this happens, it is a bit like a juggling act. Try not to be hard on yourself if you feel you are not handling it well. It is an ongoing process and rarely do parents get it right first time — but it does get better. If you have continuing negative feelings towards your toddler, seek professional help.

If your older child is hyperactive or unpredictable and likely to disturb the baby during sleep time, put a gate on your baby's room. Explain to the sibling that the newborn is still learning how to sleep alone and therefore needs the gate to keep them safe.

While the new baby sleeps, suggest the toddler choose an activity to do with you.

How Babies Communicate

Crying/grizzling is your baby's primary way of communicating. It plays an important role in expression, development and finding sleep. As time passes, your baby will find other ways of communicating, for example, by making eye contact, smiling and cooing, which will in turn reduce their need to cry/grizzle for attention.

At a very young age, babies do not see themselves as being separate from their parents — they mirror parents' emotions and facial expressions.

While scientists have been debating babies' understanding of facial expressions since Darwin's day, there is a growing body of evidence that suggests that, within the first few days after birth, newborns are sensitive to the characteristics of faces that are likely to maximise their chances of interacting with other 'members of their species'[5].

Crying/grizzling
- Crying/grizzling is not always a negative communication.
- A baby under 12 weeks has limited ways to convey feelings, needs and discomfort or pain so it is quite normal for them to cry/grizzle.
- They may be hungry, tired or overtired, cold, too hot or maybe they simply want company.
- Often babies cry/grizzle before falling asleep.
- Some newborns cry/grizzle with the sensation of passing urine or during a bowel motion.
- Some days your baby may cry/grizzle for no discernible reason!

A baby under 12 weeks is too vulnerable to be left alone to cry so, whatever the reason, you should always respond. The 'leave to cry', non-responsive approach goes against nurturing and can lead to other problems, such as sleeping and feeding issues. It is vital at this young age that their cries are responded to.

When your baby cries you may be surprised by the pitch, intensity or volume. Your ability to stay calm is key in dealing with this.

Never leave a baby under 12 weeks to cry/
grizzle for more than five minutes. I cannot
stress this enough (unless it is necessary for
the safety of the baby or caregiver).

Many parents comment that one of the greatest fears is not being able to tell *why* their baby is crying. If you find yourself at a loss, ask yourself:
- Are they tired or overtired? Remember, an overtired baby tends to cry louder and longer.
- Do they need to be held to sleep in your arms? Hold your baby in the 'engulf hold' (see page 58). Try not to rock or jiggle — instead use small movements such as cupping and patting that can be replicated in a bassinet or cot (see page 60).
- Do they want to suck (but are not hungry)? Offer a dummy/pacifier for comfort — babies in pain like to comfort-suck.

If you haven't already done so, ask yourself:
- Are they hungry?
- Do they need to be burped?
- Does their nappy need changing?

As you get to know your baby, you will learn how to read their cues. In the meantime, trust your instincts and capabilities to see you through.

If you feel you are not coping with the level of your baby's cry, be sure to seek professional help to put your mind at rest.

Other Noises Your Baby May Make
Newborns are surprisingly noisy. Even at this young age babies sniff, sneeze, yawn, squeak, gurgle, hum and make other one-off sounds. Breathing can often be irregular as their respiratory systems are still developing. Some are noisy sleepers while others are quiet.

Inconsolable Babies
Don't be put off by a comment like 'You just have one of those babies.' Continue to search for someone who will listen to you!

43

PART TWO
Sleeping and Settling

Sleep is a Nutrient

Newborns do not have the ability to self-settle (self-soothe) without your help until between 12 and 16 weeks of age. Until then, they need your nurturing and guidance to help them learn the skills — some learn this skill earlier than others.

- Babies need to be guided to learn how to self-settle (sleep) and resettle (stay asleep).
- Most newborns will sleep on average 16 hours out of 24.
- Ideally, by 12 weeks babies will have the ability to sleep for stretches of six to eight hours at night.
- There is no such thing as a baby who doesn't need much sleep, however each baby is an individual and sleep patterns will vary.

Why Do Newborn Babies Sleep So Much?
Sleep is a nutrient and is as vital to your baby's wellbeing as food. Neuroscientists have found that much of your baby's complex brain development occurs in the weeks immediately before birth and continues at an extraordinary rate throughout the first year of life — much of it while sleeping. At no other point in life does this staggering level of brain development take place.

Sleep is a Learned Behaviour
Some parents assume that their baby instinctively knows how to establish healthy sleep patterns, but in my experience newborns need guidance to learn how to self-settle, resettle and sleep soundly.

As a guide, most newborns will sleep approximately 16 hours in a 24-hour period and this will vary from day to day. Some need more sleep than others.

How well your baby sleeps will influence your baby's feeding rhythms and have a positive or negative effect on you and your family.

Understanding your baby's sleep cycles will help you deal with challenges in establishing a healthy sleep pattern. Your baby's sleep is composed of light, or Rapid Eye Movement (REM), sleep, and deep, or non-REM, sleep. During the light sleep phase, your baby's brain is exceptionally active, processing the day, storing information and dreaming.

Somewhere between 20 and 45 minutes, your baby eases from one sleep cycle into the next. For some babies, digestive issues wake them around the 20-minute mark. For others, the process of passing from light sleep to deep sleep (around 45 minutes) wakes them. It is during the deeper sleep cycle that vital growth hormones are released.

Babies who do not progress beyond the threshold of light sleep often fall into a pattern of short sleep cycles (catnaps) and frequent feeding cycles. For example, a baby may sleep for 45 minutes or less, then wake up crying. New parents often respond by getting them up to feed — assuming that sleep time is over rather than giving them a chance to resettle. Catnaps and frequent feeding inevitably produce an overtired, over-stimulated baby, which compounds sleeping and feeding issues.

· ·

The Two Alternating States of Sleep[6]

Rapid Eye Movement (REM) or 'active' sleep is when our brains are active and dreaming occurs. Our bodies become immobile, and breathing and heart rates are irregular.

Non Rapid Eye Movement (NREM), or 'quiet' sleep, is when blood supply to the muscles is increased, energy restored, tissue growth and repair take place and important hormones are released for growth and development.

Newborns spend about half their time in each of these states and the sleep cycle is around 45 minutes. At about six months of age, REM sleep makes up about 30 per cent of sleep.

· ·

Did you know? [7]

During their first three months, babies spend half their sleep in light sleep compared with one fifth for adults. This explains why they wake so easily.

Sleep is especially important for children as it directly impacts mental and physical development.

By the age of two, most children have spent more time asleep than awake; and overall a child will spend 40 per cent of their childhood asleep.

As parents it is your choice as to where your baby sleeps. Some parents enjoy the experience of teaching their baby to fall asleep in their arms while others prefer a bassinet or cot.

Many parents find settling in arms easier as it involves less bending over a bassinet/cot and provides an opportunity for quiet intimacy. In some families, how you settle your baby depends on others within the family — for example, where there are siblings cot settling may be more practical. Try both to see what is best for you.

Another option is to mix it up: perhaps practise bassinet/cot settling in the mornings when your energy levels are better, and opt for settling in the arms in the afternoon — often a fussy time anyway — when you can put your feet up and be with your baby.

Allowing your baby to sleep in your arms is not a cop-out. On the contrary, it instils a sense of security that makes them feel nurtured and ready for sleep.

Whatever you choose, I recommend your baby starts the sleep cycle in the cot while still awake. This gives them the chance to familiarise themselves with what will soon become their familiar sleeping place.

Again, whether you choose arms or bassinet/cot, never leave your baby alone to cry/grizzle for more than five minutes (unless it is necessary for safety). It is

Babies do not have the ability to self-settle (self-soothe) until between the ages of 12 to 16 weeks — some learn this skill earlier than others.

vital you are present to reassure them. Remember, newborns do *not* have the ability to self-settle (self-soothe) without your help until somewhere between 12 and 16 weeks of age. Until then they need your nurturing and guidance to help them learn the skills.

Safe Co-sleeping

- Sleeping with your baby is not advised if you, or your partner, are under the influence of recreational drugs or alcohol, or while smoking.
- Do not sleep with your baby lengthwise on a sofa where your baby could easily roll into the cushions or roll off onto the floor.
- Do not cover your baby with a duvet.
- Do not use pillows.
- Avoid mohair and any fabric with loose fibres and threads.

Some mothers are told that co-sleeping spoils a baby. On the contrary, I believe that there is nothing more nurturing for a baby than to be held close, sensing the rhythm of your heart, your familiar smell and the warmth of your body.

Psychologists talk about the first 12 weeks as being the phase when babies continue to identify themselves as still being part of their parent, so it makes sense to be close to each other whenever possible.

In my experience, therefore, an ideal and natural time to make the transition from co-sleeping to sleeping independently is at around 12 weeks, coinciding with the end of the 'fourth trimester'.

Where to Sleep

- In your arms.
- In a mix of arms and bassinet/cot.
- In a bassinet or cot.
- Safe co-sleeping in a bed.

49

Tools for Self-settling and Resettling

Techniques and tools to help your baby learn how to self-settle and resettle are as follows:

- swaddling
- the 'engulf hold'
- engulfing in the bassinet/cot
- shushing
- cupping
- patting
- dummies/pacifiers
- stroking
- creating their own space within your arms.

Swaddling

Studies show that swaddling enhances sleep by controlling your baby's startle (Moro) reflex and may help lower the risk of Sudden Infant Death Syndrome (SIDS).

Swaddling has many benefits but often draws debate — whether you choose to swaddle your baby or not is your choice. When done correctly, however, I believe swaddling is comforting and reassuring for newborns and helps establish settling and sleeping.

- Swaddling can be one of your baby's first sleep cues.
- Swaddling creates a cocooned feeling of security as in the womb.
- If done correctly, swaddling is not restrictive. It is best to leave the cloth flowing loose from the waist down like a gown.
- Use breathable fabrics, such as muslin, light cotton, cotton/merino or merino for both safety and comfort.
- Alternatively, use a purpose-made swaddling cloth. I like to use a swaddle cloth that measures 120 x 120 cm and is made of a natural fabric that breathes. Anything smaller will easily unravel and, as your baby grows, they will outgrow it.
- When swaddling, be sure to wrap securely around the chest area so that the cloth doesn't ride up over their face.
- Correct swaddling does not overheat babies, as long as parents don't overdress their baby, cover their head or overheat the room.
- Although some babies appear to resist being swaddled, it is worth persisting with a different style as they soon get used to it and ultimately sleep better and more securely.
- Babies who are not swaddled may wake themselves more often by their startle (Moro) reflex — flailing their arms about involuntarily.

51

The following are three different ways to swaddle a baby. Each swaddle can be done with a flat breathable cloth measuring 120 x 120 cm.

Snow Angel Swaddle — Arms-up Position
1. Fold down 15 cm of fabric from the top of the square — this will create the 'snow angel' fold, into which you will tuck your baby's raised arms.
2. Place your baby in the middle of the swaddle with shoulders positioned 5 cm lower than the top of the fold.
3. Take one of your baby's arms and tuck it up inside the fold (so you can no longer see it) then, starting at your baby's elbow, trace the raw edge of the fold outwards until you reach the corner of the swaddle cloth.
4. Take this corner and place it under your baby's body. Tuck it firmly under your baby's lower back.
5. Next, starting from the top of the nappy line, trace the raw edge outwards until you come to the edge of the cloth, and fold it across your baby's body, over the chest (no higher than the nipples) and tuck it firmly under your baby's body.
6. Repeat for the second side.

The swaddle is deliberately left loose and flowing at the base to ensure that no undue pressure is placed on the hip joints. This allows freedom of movement in both the hip and tummy area.

As you pick up your baby, be sure to anchor the edge of the swaddle firmly across your baby's back so it doesn't unravel. With both arms outstretched and tucked up under the fold, your baby resembles a snow angel.

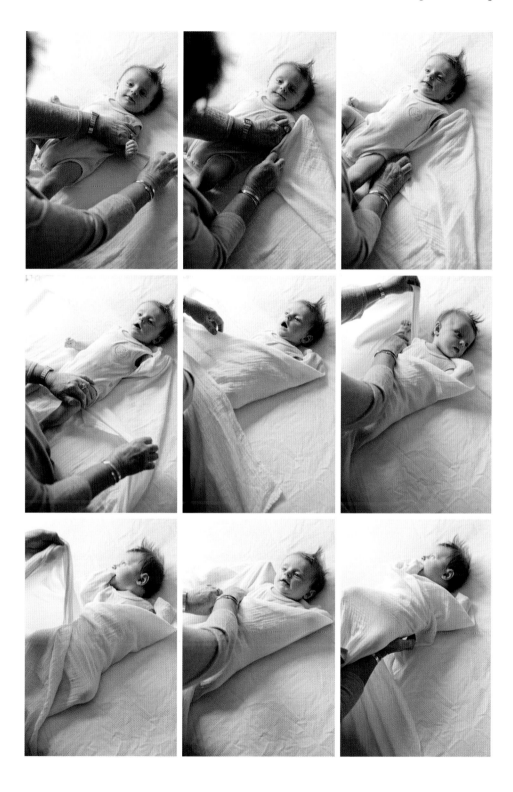

Cross Your Heart — Arms across Chest/Tummy

1. Fold down 15 cm of fabric from the top of the square.
2. Place your baby in the middle with the shoulders positioned 5 cm lower than the top fold.
3. Place one of your baby's arms across the chest.

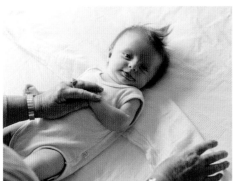 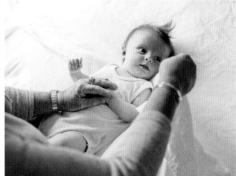

4. Gently but firmly draw the swaddle diagonally across the chest (over the folded arm) and tuck it securely under the opposite armpit, being sure to secure it all the way through to the back. (You may need to lift and roll your baby's body as you tuck it under.)

5. Next, place the opposite arm across the chest (so that it sits below or above the first arm) and, being sure to give the fabric near the ear a tug to create tension, draw the other side of the swaddle across the chest as you fold it diagonally across the front of your baby's body (over the folded arm). Take the excess fabric upwards towards the top of the shoulder and secure it firmly behind their back. Alternatively, take the excess fabric and tuck firmly behind their back.

6. The swaddle is deliberately left loose and flowing at the base to ensure that no undue pressure is placed on the hip joints. This allows freedom of movement in both the hip and tummy area.

7. As you pick up your baby, be sure to anchor the edge of the swaddle firmly across your baby's back so it doesn't unravel.

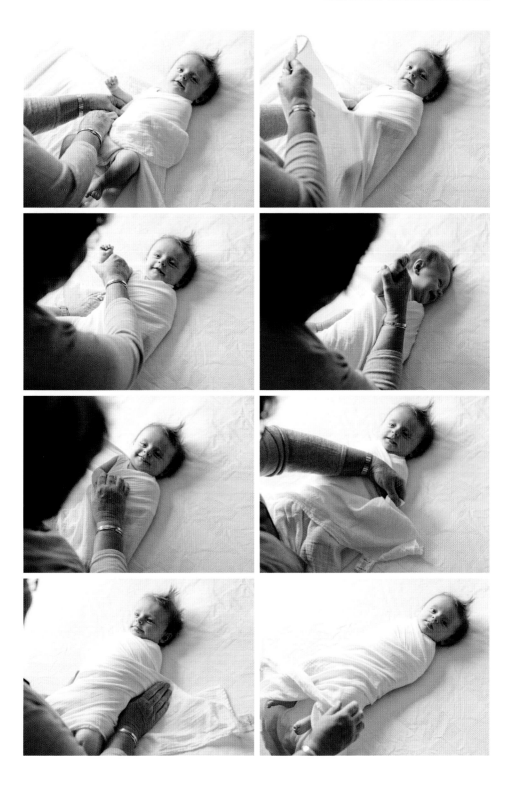

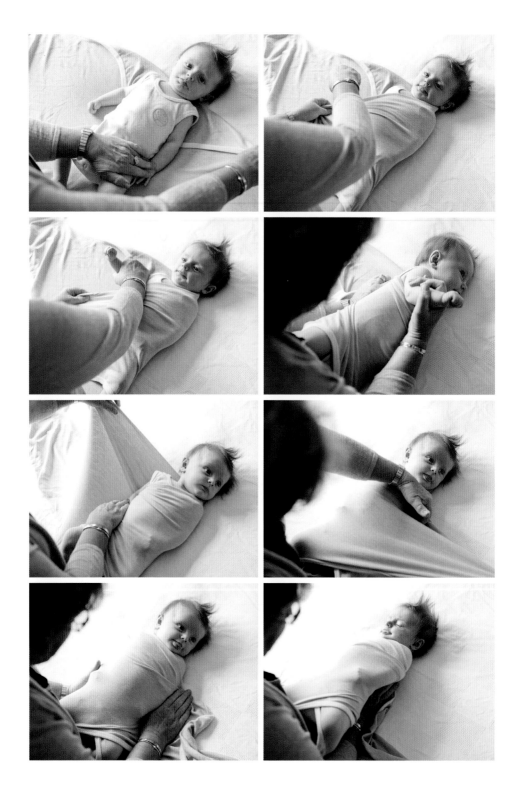

Straitjacket — Arms by Sides

1. Fold down 15 cm of fabric from the top of the square.
2. Place your baby in the middle with the shoulders positioned 5 cm lower than the top fold.
3. Starting on the first side, place one arm alongside your baby's body.
4. Gently but firmly draw the swaddle across the chest and tuck it securely under the opposite armpit, being sure to secure it all the way through to the back. (You may need to lift and roll your baby's body as you tuck it under.)
5. Place the other arm alongside your baby's body.
6. To make the swaddle as secure as possible, tug the swaddle near your baby's ear to give tension to the fabric as you wrap it across and then under your baby's body. (You may need to lift and roll your baby's body as you tuck it under.)
7. The swaddle is deliberately left loose and flowing at the base to ensure that no undue pressure is placed on the hip joints. This allows freedom of movement in both the hip and tummy area.
8. As you pick up your baby, be sure to anchor the edge of the swaddle firmly across your baby's back so it doesn't unravel.

Other Types of Swaddles

There are other ways to swaddle your baby. When choosing which methods best suit your baby, a key point to consider is how much freedom of movement the swaddle provides.

Various swaddles provide different levels of physical and emotional comfort, and much will depend on your baby's personality.

Leaving the swaddle flowing loose from the waist down allows your baby to move their hips and legs (to help gas release and digestive issues) and ensures there is no undue pressure on the hips. Newborn joints are very flexible (because of the hormone relaxin) therefore avoid swaddles that are folded up at the base, or too narrow or restrictive in the leg area.

Of the many modern purpose-made swaddles available today, my favourites are the Snugglewrap and Snugglesac from Dimples by Jane Anne (www.dimples.co.nz).

At around 12 weeks, your baby's startle (Moro) reflex becomes a controlled movement. At this time — or when your baby is ready — you can try swaddling with one arm out of the wrap, progressing to both arms out, eventually transferring them to a sleeping bag.

57

Engulfing

The word 'engulf' means to surround. With the 'engulf hold' the emphasis is on drawing your baby close in to your body to provide as much contact as possible.

Instructions

Taking into account the fact that I am left-handed, you might wish to try using the opposite side and reversing the actions. Work out which feels more comfortable, but bear in mind you will be using your free hand to do the cupping and patting movements.

1. Pick up your baby so they are facing you and draw them in towards your right shoulder so that their head is resting on your upper arm with their face nestling towards your armpit (their body is diagonal to your body).
2. Wrap your right arm across your baby's shoulders and take hold of their upper arm or shoulder (the one closest to your face) to firmly support them.
3. With your left hand, turn your baby towards you by rolling their bottom upwards and inwards, so that their entire body is pressed firmly into your body — leaving no gaps (it should be impossible to slip a sheet of paper between you). Your baby's face is resting on your upper arm and turned inwards towards your body. Babies who are light-sensitive tend to bury their face into your armpit.
4. Place your palm on your baby's bottom to support them.

Benefits of the Engulf Hold

- The engulf hold is nurturing and reassuring for babies — it provides warmth, security and intimacy and an opportunity to be near your heartbeat and familiar scent.
- It positions a baby at such an angle that their head is higher than their body — ideal for reflux babies when helping them find sleep.
- For breastfeeding mothers, this hold ensures that their baby's face is not too close to the breast where they could easily be tempted towards feeding again.

Engulfing in the Bassinet/Cot

Engulfing in the bassinet/cot can be done two ways: while your baby is lying on their back, or lying on their side facing away from you. This technique helps establish as much contact as possible without having to hold them.

When engulfing in the bassinet/cot, is important that you stand to the side of your baby and away from their face, out of their eye line, ideally no higher than their waist level.

If you choose to comfort while your baby is lying on their back, then engulf (in the bassinet/cot) by placing your hand gently but firmly on your baby's chest and arms. With your other hand start cupping (see page 60).

Alternatively, you can do this while your baby is lying on their side. Turn them so they are facing away from you and place one hand firmly over their shoulder and arms (not their waist) to 'half engulf' your baby. Use your free hand to start cupping.

Shushing

Shushing is a long, low sound, resembling air being released from a tyre. Ideally, it is loud enough for it to be calming. Lower the volume as your baby settles. It is thought that babies respond to shushing because it is similar to the sound in the womb. In practice I avoid shushing close to the baby's ear — I tend to shush over their body instead.

Cupping and Patting

With all cupping and patting techniques, keep the rhythm firm and steady. It's vital that your body remains still as if it's their bed. Don't forget to breathe! Staying relaxed and calm helps.

Cupping

Cupping mimics your baby's heartbeat, replaces larger movements, and reassures your baby of your presence during self-settling and resettling. It plays a key role in engulfing in the arms and engulfing in the bassinet/cot. It is a gentle but firm movement. Use it to replace walking, rocking, jiggling, swinging — all of which are movements that cannot be replicated in a bassinet/cot.

Cupping is a specific technique done with your palm slightly cupped that combines a gentle but firm rhythmic action with a short thrust or shunt forward of your baby's body. Think of it as two movements in one: a cup and a push without removing your hand from your baby's body.

There are various ways to cup your baby and it's worth trying them all to see which work best for your baby. The standard way is to hold your baby securely in the engulf hold and rhythmically cup your baby's buttocks.

For babies that don't respond to or don't like this movement, or for babies suffering from reflux or colic, try cupping the area above the nappy line on the baby's lower back. I find babies with reflux and colic often respond to this variation.

Another way is to combine a 'cup' with a 'roll', almost as if you are coming from underneath your baby's body to 'cup and thrust' while adding a rotation

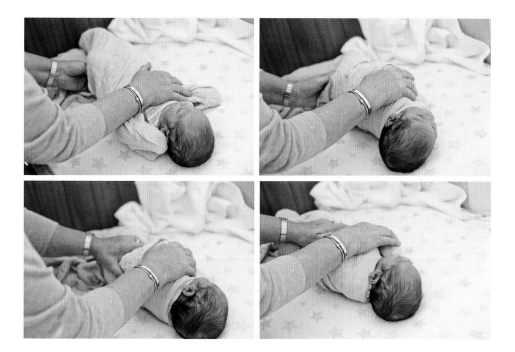

as well. This can be done on the side of their bottom, or further up the side at the top of their nappy. Don't be afraid to experiment to find out what your baby likes and what works for you.

The difference between cupping and patting is that when cupping, your hand stays connected to your baby's body throughout whereas when patting, you remove your hand.

Patting

61

Patting is a firm, repetitive, rhythmic action done with your palm flat on your baby's bottom or thigh area.

Dummies/Pacifiers

Dummies (or pacifiers) can be useful to help settle your baby. However, I believe if you 'plug' your baby as soon as they go to bed, you may take away the opportunity for them to try to settle by themselves. In my experience, giving your baby a dummy/pacifier straight away can cause more crying than if you let them cry/grizzle first before giving it to them.

Keep in mind that all babies are born with a sucking reflex — a natural urge to suck as a way to calm and soothe themselves — which diminishes at around six months. By this time, most babies grow out of the need for a dummy/pacifier to be used as a settling tool.

Stroking

Gently stroking your baby's face is soothing and may help your baby to relax and fall asleep. There are many variations. One I often use is to stroke slowly and gently with a fingertip downwards from the centre of your baby's forehead to the bridge of their nose. Repeat until your baby goes to sleep.

Another option is to stroke with your fingertip from the edge of your baby's eyebrow downwards and over the temples to the top of the cheekbone. Repeat until your baby goes to sleep.

Creating a space

Some babies need their own space to help them relax and fall asleep, even while in your arms, especially babies who are easily distracted or overstimulated by environmental factors. I find that draping a muslin cloth over your shoulder and the top of their body can help an alert baby calm down, relax and fall asleep. The cloth should always be lightweight and of a breathable fabric. Don't use anything dense or heavy.

Tools That Should Not Become Props

Babies have an amazing capacity to learn and respond well to sleep cues. For this reason, it is a good idea to 'start as you mean to go on', and teach your baby how to self-settle without using props.

The following practices run the risk of taking away your baby's chance to self-settle and resettle and can become difficult habits to break:
- feeding to sleep
- using large movements that cannot be replicated in a bassinet or cot
- offering a dummy/pacifier before your baby has had a chance to self-settle or resettle
- using white noise.

Feeding to sleep is a personal choice. There are, of course, pros and cons for both. If you choose to feed your baby to sleep because it seems the easy way, it is worth first thinking it through. Some babies feed to sleep for months then, one day, for no obvious reason, wean themselves and are able to self-settle and sleep well. Others, however, love to be fed to sleep for as long as parents are willing to offer it and come to rely on it.

When making the decision, perhaps ask yourself:
- Will I be happy to still be feeding my baby to sleep in six, 12 or 18 months' time?
- Will I have the time available to do so?
- Am I happy to teach my one-year-old how to self-settle and resettle?

If the boxes are ticked, then by all means forge ahead.

Movement that cannot be replicated in a bassinet/cot (including bouncing on a Swiss ball, walking, jiggling and rocking), white noise, and offering dummies/pacifiers to 'plug' your baby, all serve to take away your baby's chance to self-settle on their own accord.

While I encourage parents to 'stop, think and act' I am also fully supportive of parents making their own informed choices. Remember, when it comes to parenting, there are no hard and fast rules, and there is no right or wrong way — but some ways are easier than others.

In my experience, it is easier to teach a baby *under* 16 weeks to self-settle (using small movements such as cupping and patting), than one aged 18 months or older.

Rocking, Jiggling and Pacing

While some parents comment that rocking and pacing seem to help calm their baby, more often this activity actually helps calm the parents — and once the parents are calm, their babies follow suit. It takes TACT — time, acceptance, consistency and touch — for parents to accept and adapt to changing from using larger movements (rocking, jiggling, pacing, etc.) to smaller movements that can be replicated in the bassinet/cot.

Babies don't need to be rocked in a stroller, driven in a car or walked around the block to encourage them to sleep. What they want is warmth and familiarity to comfort them.

Not only do these activities take away your baby's chance to self-settle, but as your baby grows these routines become more demanding, time-consuming and physically taxing on you. For instance, what was initially a five-minute walk around the block can end up taking an hour, encroaching on precious settling and sleeping time.

65

Self-settling

It bears repeating that newborns do not *have the ability to self-settle (self-soothe) without your help until somewhere between 12 and 16 weeks of age. Until then, they need your nurturing and guidance to help them learn the skills.*

Self-settling is all about nurturing! I can't stress this enough. Self-settling — also known as self-soothing — helps your baby learn how to fall asleep unaided. It enhances your baby's quality of sleep and is the key to helping your baby establish healthy sleep patterns.

Self-settling:
- lays the foundations for babies to learn how to fall asleep independently, without the use of aids or props
- offers an opportunity to engulf your baby quietly in your arms — with no words, movement or props — instilling a confidence and sense of security that will help them find sleep
- requires TACT — time, acceptance, consistency and touch — as well as repetition, patience and commitment.

Self-settling means stepping aside to allow your baby to find sleep independently, either in your arms or in the bassinet/cot. It might be for as little as half a minute or longer (up to a maximum of five minutes), depending on what you feel comfortable with, before you feel the time is right for you to intervene and support them to sleep.

As adults we have choices at bedtime: we may read a book, meditate, watch TV, have a bath, or chat to our partner before we go to sleep. For a sleepy baby, a most natural response is to cry.

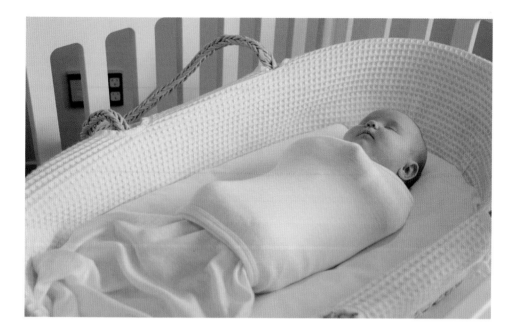

Although at times it can be difficult for parents to listen to their baby crying as they attempt to find sleep, it is worth keeping in mind that as long as they are well, not in pain and being nurtured, these small intervals of crying — with you present — are a positive and necessary part of your baby's progress. It will be worth it in the long run!

Self-settling is a learning process that begins as early as day one and evolves as your baby grows and their needs change. It can be done in your arms or in the cot — whichever works best for you and your baby.

From the outset, it is important that parents understand that most babies will *not* have the ability to self-settle (self-soothe) without your help until somewhere between 12 and 16 weeks at the earliest. Until then, they need your nurturing and guidance to encourage them to learn the skills.

If, during the first 12 weeks, you are able to spend time holding them in your arms or sitting with them to support and guide them as they learn to find sleep, your efforts will go a long way in laying foundations for healthy sleep patterns.

It is likely that man hours will be spent supporting and comforting them — see it as a valuable opportunity to nurture your baby and bond with them as you discover which sleep cues your baby likes best and responds to.

Positive Sleep Cues

It is important parents realise what self-settling is *not* ... It is *not* controlled crying or sleep training. It does *not* involve leaving your baby to cry it out alone to finally fall asleep depleted, distressed and exhausted.

67

Self-settling is *always* done with nurturing. (I want to shout this from the rooftops!) The objective of self-settling is to provide your newborn with a sense of feeling completely protected and emotionally secure in their environment so they can switch off and fall asleep contented.

When it comes to settling a baby, my advice is to keep it simple. In my experience, the most effective way to help your baby fall asleep is to sit quietly and use small and repetitive techniques, such as cupping and patting that can be done in your arms or in the cot. These subtle but firm movements are calming for a newborn and, when the time is right, can be gently tapered off so that eventually your baby will be able to fall asleep without the need for them.

One of my favourite expressions is 'Don't start anything in your arms that you can't replicate in a bassinet/cot.' If circumstances allow, I encourage parents to predominantly self-settle their babies in their arms for the first 12 weeks, then follow their instincts when deciding whether to self-settle in the bassinet/cot.

Perhaps your baby prefers certain settling techniques over others, or sleeps better at different times of the day. As they grow, self-settling becomes an integral part of their sleep ritual, and it is a skill they will have for life.

If exclusively self-settling in arms, ideally aim to introduce self-settling in the bassinet/cot no later than 12 weeks — it makes it easier for all. Generally, it comes down to a mother's gut instinct, which often coincides with their baby's growing confidence.

Be patient and *don't forget*: babies simply do not have the ability to self-settle (self-soothe) until somewhere between 12 and 16 weeks. Once parents are aware of this, they can enjoy the process and be less fraught with expectation.

A Reminder of What Self-settling is Not
- Self-settling is *not* controlled crying or sleep training. Self-settling is always done with nurturing.
- The objective of self-settling is to provide your newborn with a sense of feeling completely protected and emotionally secure in their environment so they can switch off and fall asleep contented.
- Self-settling does *not* involve leaving your baby to cry it out alone to finally fall asleep due to stress and exhaustion.

Self-settling is always done with nurturing. (I want to shout this from the rooftops!)

What to Expect When Self-settling in Arms or a Bassinet/Cot

Your baby's cry/grizzle could intensify for a few minutes before tapering off, or could stop and start like a car engine. Or they might cry for a bit, then settle and fall asleep.

Some days their cry/grizzle might seem more forceful and tug at your heartstrings, while on other days you may feel more confident and be able to deal with it better. Go with the flow.

Whatever the case, keep in mind that crying or grizzling at bedtime is normal and it is your baby's way of expressing themselves and unwinding from the day's activities. To the best of your ability, remain composed and try not to feel panic or self-doubt.

The 'Five Minute' Guide

How long you let your baby cry or grizzle before intervening depends on what you feel comfortable with. It's very much bound up with instinct and your emotional pull to comfort your baby.

As a guide, for babies aged zero to six weeks my rule of thumb is to allow a minute for each week of age — but be sure not to exceed a maximum of five minutes. It is crucial that your baby never feels abandoned — five minutes is an eternity to small babies and to parents.

When starting out, you may feel that one or two crying intervals are enough, before you choose to comfort them to sleep. If this is your feeling, go with it. As your baby grows and gets used to self-settling, it's up to you to extend the intervals according to what feels comfortable before responding.

69

Steps to Self-settling

The following sequences form the basis of your self-settling routine both day and night whether you do it in your arms or in the bassinet/cot:

- Swaddle.
- Darken the room.
- Place your baby in their bassinet/cot while still awake — whether self-settling in arms or cot it is ideal that they begin the cycle in the bassinet/cot.
- 'Dump and run, don't hover like a helicopter' — in other words, leave the room quickly and quietly.
- When your baby cries/grizzles, stop, think and act. In the beginning, it is important that you respond immediately. From here, you have a choice to self-settle your baby in your arms, or in the bassinet/cot, or a mix of both, using the steps below as a guideline.

Self-settling Your Baby in Your Arms

If at the end of this cycle they are still not asleep, offer a dummy/pacifier and resume cupping and shushing until they fall asleep. At some stage during the settling process there will come a point when you and your baby connect and your baby responds to the cupping and shushing. Once this happens, be sure to continue cupping and shushing until your baby falls asleep.

In my experience, it takes around 20 minutes for a baby to find their sleep — that's four lots of five minutes. Ideally, your baby is asleep before this.

Meanwhile, allowing your baby to sleep in your arms is not a cop-out. On the contrary, it instils a sense of security that makes your baby feel nurtured and ready for sleep.

- Pick up your baby from the bassinet/cot and engulf them.
- Choose a quiet place to sit that will provide good support for your back and arms so you can see it through. Your comfort is vital as it is likely that you will be sitting and holding your baby for some time.
- Imagine your body is your baby's bed — remain still, no rocking. Stay calm and allow the warmth of your body to nurture your baby, absorbing their cries and tension.
- Avoid talking or making eye contact — both are stimulating and provide your baby with a reason to want to stay awake.
- Allow your baby to cry/grizzle for one to five minutes ... or whatever you feel comfortable with.
- At the end of the interval, reassure with cupping and shushing.
- Comfort time should ideally be shorter than crying time. For instance, if you choose to let them cry for two minutes, comfort for one minute.
- Stop cupping and shushing.
- Allow them to cry/grizzle for one to five minutes (although this interval can be shorter than the first round of crying/grizzling, it should not be longer).
- At the end of the interval, intervene by cupping and shushing (another option is to offer a dummy/pacifier). If they continue to cry, stop cupping and shushing.
- Allow them to cry/grizzle for one to five minutes (although this interval can be shorter than the first round of crying/grizzling, it should not be longer).
- At the end of the interval, resume cupping and shushing (another option is to offer a dummy/pacifier).
- If at the end of this cycle they are still not asleep, offer a dummy/pacifier and resume cupping and shushing until they fall asleep.

Self-settling Your Baby in the Bassinet/Cot

Allow them to cry/grizzle for one to five minutes. If at the end of this cycle they are still not asleep, offer a dummy and resume cupping and shushing until they fall asleep. At some stage during the settling process there will come a point when you and your baby connect and your baby responds to the cupping and shushing. Once this happens, be sure to continue cupping and shushing until your baby falls asleep. As with self-settling in your arms, in my experience it takes around 20 minutes for a baby to find their sleep — that's four lots of five minutes. Ideally, your baby is asleep before this.

Remember, most babies do *not* have the ability to self-settle (self-soothe) without your help until somewhere between 12 and 16 weeks of age. Until then, they need your nurturing and guidance to help them learn the skills.

- Place your baby in their bassinet/cot while still awake.
- Leave the room — 'dump and run, don't hover like a helicopter'.
- Leave to cry/grizzle for up to one minute.
- Then go back into their room, pick them up and burp them.
- Return them to the bassinet/cot. Here you have options: leave the room, *or* stay in the room with your hands on your baby (while remaining still — no movement), *or* step back quietly and stay in the room.
- When they cry, allow them to cry/grizzle for one to five minutes.
- At the end of the interval, reassure them with cupping and shushing, and engulf in the bassinet/cot.
- When engulfing in the bassinet/cot, is important that you stand to the side of your baby and away from their face, out of their eye line, ideally no higher than their waist level.
- If you choose to comfort while your baby is lying on their back, then engulf them (in the bassinet/cot) by placing your hand gently but firmly on your baby's chest and arms. Alternatively, you can do this while your baby is lying on their side. Turn them so they are facing away from you and place one hand firmly over their shoulder and arms (not their waist) to 'half engulf' your baby. Use your free hand to start cupping.
- If they continue to cry, stop cupping and shushing — you can either keep your hands on them (no movement) or step back quietly and stay in the room. Alternatively, leave the room.

- Allow them to cry/grizzle for one to five minutes (although this interval can be shorter than the first round of crying/grizzling, it should not be longer).
- At the end of the interval, intervene by cupping and shushing (another option is to offer a dummy/pacifier).
- If they continue to cry, stop cupping and shushing — you can either keep your hands on them (no movement) or step back and stay in the room. Alternatively, leave the room.
- Allow them to cry/grizzle for one to five minutes (although this interval can be shorter than the first round of crying/grizzling, it should not be longer).
- At the end of the interval, intervene by cupping and shushing (you may wish to re-offer a dummy/pacifier).
- If they continue to cry, stop cupping and shushing — you can either keep your hands on them (no movement) or step back and stay in the room. Alternatively, leave the room.
- Allow them to cry/grizzle for one to five minutes. If at the end of this cycle they are still not asleep (as with self-settling in your arms) offer a dummy/ pacifier and resume cupping and shushing until they fall asleep. In my experience it takes around 20 minutes for a baby to find their sleep — that's four lots of five minutes. Ideally, your baby is asleep before this!
- Once you sense that your baby is asleep, remove your hand from their chest and lighten the patting until eventually you can withdraw your hand, continue as if patting the air.
- If your baby stays asleep, gently roll them onto their back (if they have not naturally done this) and leave the room.
- If, as you exit, your baby stirs or you hear them crying once you have left the room, return and repeat the process.
- If your baby refuses to settle, you may choose to pick them up and self-settle them in your arms (see page 70).
- Be sure not to lay your baby on their side when wrapped in a straitjacket swaddle (this is to prevent your baby's full body weight pressing on their arm).
- Picking up your baby to comfort them is not a cop-out. It's an important part of nurturing.

Resettling

Babies do not have the tools to resettle themselves until the age of 12 to 16 weeks — it is a learned behaviour and it takes time for your baby to learn how to do it. However, like self-settling, the sooner you choose to start gently teaching them the basics of resettling, the sooner they will learn how to do it.

- Resettling is the key to helping your baby progress from their first sleep cycle to their second sleep cycle.
- A baby who does not learn how to resettle may wake frequently during the night.
- A drowsy baby is easier to resettle than one who is awake.
- Remaining calm and focused speeds the resettling process.
- Resettling takes time, acceptance, consistency and touch — TACT.
- Babies who are not taught how to resettle tend to sleep shorter sleep cycles.

The Importance of Resettling

Resettling is often overlooked yet it plays a vital role in teaching your baby to sleep through the night. As adults, most of us wake during the night, roll over and return to sleep totally unaware that we have woken. This is because we have our usual sleep cues — a darkened room, customary sounds and a familiar bed — that make us feel safe enough to fall back to sleep. Newborns have yet to create these positive cues and need support from you to do so.

Most babies stir or wake when progressing from light to deep sleep. For some, this happens after 20 minutes (normally due to digestive issues). For others it happens around the 45-minute mark.

For example, some babies wake up 20 minutes after going down, often due to tummy pains, cramping or gas and, once picked up and burped, can be resettled by engulfing, either in arms or bassinet/cot.

Babies that wake after 45 minutes or so, usually wake as they progress from one sleep cycle to the next — something I call 'fluttering' — and need help to continue sleeping.

If your baby wakes around 45 minutes and does not go back to sleep – or isn't given the chance to return to sleep – this sleep cycle is commonly referred to as a catnap or one sleep cycle.

Eventually, babies who have been given the opportunity to resettle learn how to progress from one sleep cycle to two sleep cycles — or light sleep to deep sleep — without waking. On the occasions they do wake, they are often calmer and easier to resettle because they have learnt to do this.

In my experience, a baby who does not learn how to resettle often has short sleep cycles and wakes frequently without the ability to fall back to sleep.

Resettling can be done in your arms or in the bassinet/cot — whichever works best for you and your baby. It requires no extra gadgets, props or aids.

The same pre-sleep cues that help calm and settle babies for sleep will also help them resettle when they wake. As with self-settling, your presence and patience during resettling goes a long way towards reassuring your baby that their world is safe and you are there to meet their every need.

Believe me, resettling *is* hard — but it is a lot easier to teach them when they are younger as opposed to when they are older.

Stay Calm

Resettling can sometimes demand more patience than the initial settling — I often put this down to the fact that once the baby wakes, parents are over-anxious for them to stay asleep while meanwhile they have perked up a little following their nap and are ready to play.

As much as you can, stay calm and composed. Babies take their signals from you by reading your body language so the more relaxed you are the easier it will be to resettle them. If I am struggling to get a baby to resettle, I sometimes fall asleep, and find the baby falls asleep too.

Try Not to Let Your Baby Wake Fully

Resettling is all about timing. Ideally, try not to let your baby wake fully — a sleepy baby is much easier to resettle than one who is fully awake and engaged with the world. Once you get to know your baby's rhythm, try pre-empting their

waking and start resettling them as soon as they stir. Keep in mind that as they grow (beyond 12 weeks) you will, when the time is right, be able to step back to allow them to resettle without your help. However, on the occasions they cannot do it on their own, intervene and help them.

The Less Fuss, the Better

If they do wake, resettle them with as little fuss as possible. Try not to give them a reason to want to stay awake, in other words, avoid talking and eye contact — both are stimulating. While this might seem like tough love, it is in your baby's best interests that you give them the chance to fall back to sleep. Keep in mind that your goal is to persuade them to sleep through. Let your body communicate with them rather than you talking or making eye contact. It is the same for us as adults: if someone engages with us when we are trying to sleep, it makes it harder for us to get back to sleep.

Resettling, Props and Movement

Like self-settling, resettling is infinitely more effective without the use of sleep props or movement. Resist the urge to rely on these to coax your baby to sleep as they interfere with your baby's chance to learn how to resettle independently. However, on the occasions you cannot resettle your baby, use whatever props are necessary to get you through.

77

Resettling and Feeding

Resist the temptation to feed as a means to resettle your baby. Feeding encroaches on valuable sleep time and produces an overtired, cranky baby who becomes more difficult to resettle. It also becomes something they rely upon to fall asleep and takes away their ability to learn how to resettle independently.

More than likely your baby *isn't* hungry but wants comfort and, unintentionally, you end up feeding for comfort instead of hunger. On these occasions, try cupping, shushing and offering a dummy/pacifier while your baby is in the bassinet/cot.

On the few occasions when you're unable to resettle them, then start the next awake cycle and feed them.

If your baby seems to settle easily but has difficulty resettling, perhaps ask yourself these questions:
- Is my baby light-sensitive — is the room dark enough or would black-out blinds help?
- Did I allow my baby to wake fully — was I too slow to respond?
- Am I using props that interfere with resettling?
- Has my baby been burped properly?
- Are there too many distractions?
- Am I calm?
- Is the room too cold or too hot?

Sequences for Resettling

Self-settling and resettling your baby can be demanding, especially at the end of the day when you are frazzled and in need of sleep yourself. Like any skill, it requires time, acceptance, consistency and touch (TACT) along with practice, repetition and commitment, from both you and your baby. On the positive side, your patient efforts in these first few months will reap rewards for everyone, as eventually your baby will be able to sleep anywhere and have the skills to respond well to any changes or disruption to daily routine.

Keep in mind that this is a time of great change as your baby endeavours to adapt to life outside the womb. Be as patient and as sensitive as you can to help ease this transition.

Resettling in Your Arms

Once they have resettled at this point you may choose to let your baby sleep the entire nap in your arms or you may wish to transfer them to the cot. An ideal time to put them in their cot is after 75 minutes or so, by which stage they will be less likely to wake.

- As soon as they stir, resume cupping and shushing and offer the dummy/pacifier, if using one.
- As they progress to their second sleep cycle it's likely you will feel a shift in their body weight.
- At this point you may choose to let your baby sleep the entire nap in your arms, or you may wish to transfer them to the bassinet/cot. An ideal time to put them in their bassinet/cot is after around 75 minutes, by which stage they will be less likely to wake. If they do wake, however, you have options:
  1. to resettle in the bassinet/cot
  2. to start their next wake cycle.

Transferring Your Baby from Your Arms to the Cot

- As you stand up to transfer your baby to the cot, start cupping.
- Once in the cot, you can either leave the room, *or*, if they stir, start cupping, shushing and engulfting in the bassinet/cot. Offer a dummy/pacifier, if using one.
- Remember, when engulfing in the bassinet/cot, it's important that you stand to the side of your baby and away from their face, out of their eye line, ideally no closer than their waist.
- If comforting while your baby is lying on their back, place your hand gently but firmly on your baby's chest and arms and with your other hand start cupping.
- To engulf in the bassinet/cot while they are on their side, be sure to turn them so they are facing away from you, then place one hand firmly over their shoulder and arm (not their waist) to 'half engulf' your baby. Use your free hand to start cupping.
- When you sense they are asleep, remove your hand from your baby's chest and reduce the patting until eventually you withdraw your hand, as if patting the air.
- Leave the room.

If they wake again, you have two options:

1. To go back into the room and resettle — either in bassinet/cot or arms.
2. If you are unable to resettle them, pick them up and start their next awake cycle. There is no 'rule book' that governs how often you should feed your baby, but on these occasions, if your baby is not sleeping, the next step is to begin their wake cycle and feed, regardless of how much time has passed since the last feed.

Resettling in the Bassinet/Cot

In the early days, it is important to respond as soon as your baby shows signs of stirring, as it is much easier to resettle a sleepy baby than one who is awake. You may like to use a monitor to help gauge when they stir.

The following can be done in the cot with your baby positioned on their back, or on their side facing away from you:

- When engulfing in the cot (on their back or side) it's important that you stand to the side of your baby and away from their face, out of their eye line, ideally no closer than their waist.
- Start cupping and shushing, offer a dummy/pacifier if using one.
- If comforting while your baby is lying on their back, place your hand gently but firmly on your baby's chest and arms and, with your other hand, start cupping.
- Alternatively, turn them so they are facing away from you, and place one hand firmly over their shoulder and arms (not their waist) to 'half engulf' your baby. Use your free hand to start cupping.
- Once they are asleep, remove your hand from their chest and lighten the cupping/patting until eventually you withdraw your hand, continuing to cup/pat as if patting the air. If your baby is lying on their side, once you take your hands off, they will roll back onto their back, but if this doesn't happen, then gently do it for them.
- If your baby stays asleep, leave the room, quietly.
- If, as you exit, your baby stirs — or once you've left the room you hear them cry or grizzle — return and repeat the process.
- If your baby does not resettle, you may choose to pick them up and self-settle them in your arms.

- As your baby grows, it's good to step back and give your baby the chance to try to resettle without your help. At first this may only be for a few minutes, but gradually you will be able to increase this timeframe until eventually your baby will get used to resettling independently. In my experience, the ideal age to start doing this is between 12 and 16 weeks, or even slightly older.
- Be sure not to lay your baby on their side when wrapped in a straitjacket swaddle (this is to prevent your baby's full body weight pressing on their arm).

Waking Up the Room

Waking up is as important as going to sleep. It is a good idea to teach your baby from a young age that their bassinet/cot is a safe haven and somewhere where, as they grow, they will be happy to wake and play.

Rather than rushing in to pick them up, go in and reassure them with your presence. Greet them with your voice and walk over to the window to open the curtains a little to give the cue that 'light is for wake time'.

This gives them a chance to be in their own space for a moment while your presence and soothing voice signals to them that they are safe. As they grow, you can increase these intervals slightly, perhaps taking the time to prepare the change table or put away clothes, while chatting to your baby.

If you go directly to them and pick them up every time they cry, they will come to expect this response and rely on it for their security.

81

As with self-settling, resettling offers an opportunity to nurture and bond with your baby.

- Resettling requires TACT — time, acceptance, consistency and touch — plus patience, repetition and commitment.
- Many hours will be spent holding your baby or sitting with them as they learn to find sleep.
- When the going gets tough, remind yourself of the pay-off in the long run.

Creating a Rhythm

In the first 12 weeks, time is largely divided between sleeping and feeding. Think of it as fitting together two major pieces of a jigsaw that influence and affect each other.

Babies who sleep well, feed well; and those who feed well, sleep well.

The best routine is one that reflects the needs of both you and your baby — and one that fits into your world.

- Feeding and sleeping go hand in hand and will form the basis of your baby's daily rhythm.
- Aim for flexibility with some structure.
- Babies aged zero to six weeks will ideally be up for no longer than 45 minutes to an hour at a time.
- Babies aged six to 12 weeks will ideally be up for no longer than 60 to 90 minutes at a time.
- During the day, aim for somewhere between two and a quarter and four hours between feeds.
- Your daytime rhythm affects your night-time rhythm.

The First Two Weeks
Initially, there will be little differentiation between day and night. Time awake will largely be a blend of feeding, changing your baby's nappy, burping and cuddles, before settling them for sleep. As they grow, the awake intervals will gradually increase to include floor and playtime. At this stage, the rhythm is: *baby cries, you respond, you feed, burp, change and swaddle them, then help them to sleep.*

The Next Stage
When your baby is around 10 to 14 days old, begin introducing the concept that dark is for sleeping and light is for waking. You can do this by letting light into the room when your baby awakes from a daytime sleep, and feeding in adequate

lighting during night feeds. At this stage, it is also good to encourage them to sleep in their bassinet or cot in their room, rather than in other rooms around the house.

When sleeping, keep the room suitably darkened to give the cue that it is time for sleep.

How long your baby sleeps will determine when and how often you feed. Some babies are better sleepers than others, some have larger appetites than others, and all babies digest at different rates. In the initial weeks, most babies will wake frequently, as they are still used to feeding constantly in the womb. Feeding and sleeping rhythms will vary from day to day.

As a guide, newborns aged zero to six weeks are usually awake for no longer than 45 minutes to an hour at a time, including feeding, burping, changing the nappy and returning them to bed. While this may seem fleeting, longer periods will tire your baby and make it more difficult for you to settle and resettle them to sleep. At this young age, sleep and food are more important than play.

For those aged six to 12 weeks, this awake interval increases to 60–90 minutes, including feeding, changing and burping.

To improve your baby's sleep intervals, babies under 12 weeks should be encouraged to sleep for a minimum of 90 minutes so they are able to progress beyond light sleep to the all-important deep sleep phase, or from one sleep cycle to two sleep cycles, which happens somewhere around the 45-minute mark.

Encouraging them to reach the next sleep cycle is essential in helping set up long-term sleep patterns, and avoids catnapping and snack feeding.

Keep in mind that every baby's rhythm is unique. Some babies thrive on feeding every 90 minutes, some wake every three-and-a-quarter hours and others every two hours — all of these are fine. It all comes down to your baby's individual needs at any given time. As a parent it is good to know that this is okay.

How your baby's daily patterns evolve in the first 12 weeks will largely depend on your baby's personality, your household and other commitments you are juggling.

The Overstimulated Baby

Babies are Sponges

Some parents, without realising it, keep their babies up for too long or expose them to frenetic environments: an active household, visitors coming and going, a loud television, a dog constantly barking or the sound of your voice on the telephone.

85

It is easy to be fooled into believing that an alert and active baby requires less sleep than others. This is rarely true. It is more likely that hyperactivity is a sign of an overtired baby.

Babies are sponges and don't know their limits. While they may seem eager to be part of what is going on, it is more likely that, in reality, they are totally exhausted.

Even a seemingly inert baby picks up on implicit messages and responds to stimulation — this is how they collect and process information to make sense of their world.

Young babies cannot self-regulate — they respond better to mellow environments, including your expression, loving touch, soothing tone of voice and nurturing body language to help them settle.

Forget Tired Signs!

Some experts suggest looking for tired signs as an indication that your baby is sleepy or overtired. This can be tricky as babies are unique and it is only through getting to know your baby that you will begin to recognise these indicators.

Some babies yawn or rub their eyes or seem excessively fussy when tired yet not all do so — on the whole, babies are wonderfully inconsistent. Also, if your baby is swaddled, they won't be able to demonstrate jerky hand movements or rub their eyes. Learning to read your baby's tired signs could take weeks, maybe months — meanwhile your baby is missing out on precious sleep.

Keeping Records

As a reference, it is a good idea to keep records in a notebook, for example:
- the time of day you begin feeding
- which side you start with (if breastfeeding), or amount (for bottle feeds)
- the number of wet nappies
- the number of soiled nappies.

Your record-keeping can be as basic or detailed as you wish, although the less of a chore it is, the more likely you will update it. Keep the notebook next to your feeding chair and total the columns at midnight before starting a fresh page for a new day. The advantage of a book over an app is you have a record for life. It's also useful to refer to when another baby comes along.

With modern technology, many parents now have access to apps via the Internet for their devices. Do your research to find one that suits you and your family. [8]

When to Wake a Sleeping Baby

The old adage 'never wake a sleeping baby' is somewhat misleading.

While alert babies are unaware they need to sleep, sleepy babies are often unaware they need to wake to feed. One needs to be taught how to sleep; the other needs to learn how to wake. This is where you must guide them.

Many parents are reluctant to wake their sleeping baby from day sleeps and let them to sleep for longer, assuming they must need it. In my experience, it is best to intervene and wake them so they don't go longer than four hours between feeds. For example, if your baby's last feed began at 10 a.m., be sure to wake them by 1.45 p.m. so you are feeding by 2 p.m. Otherwise you will inevitably find yourselves wedged in a nocturnal feeding pattern, where your baby becomes accustomed to eating at night and sleeping by day. This sort of rhythm is tricky to reverse and is taxing on all of you. Keep in mind that your daytime rhythm affects your night-time rhythm.

Never Keep a Hungry Baby Waiting!

Some parents become confused because they are under the illusion that their babies should feed every three hours. This timeframe might work for some, but stretching your baby out to three-hourly intervals purely because you read it somewhere doesn't mean it is the right thing for *your* baby. My motto is never keep a hungry baby waiting. It inevitably leads to a distressed and overtired baby who is unable to feed well and sleep well. Consequently, you become flustered, tired and anxious, which only adds to your baby's stress levels.

If after your baby's appropriate time awake they still appear alert and able to stay up for longer, it is your role to guide and support them to sleep.

Feeding and Sleeping Guidelines

A feeding interval begins from the start of the previous feed and extends until the beginning of the next feed, including sleep time. Add together the time awake and the time spent sleeping — this will give the feeding interval.

The following table provides examples of feeding and sleeping intervals to give you confidence that you are on the right track.

Time Awake	Time Napping	Feeding Interval
¾ hour	1½ hours	2¼ hours
¾ hour	2 hours	2 ¾ hours
¾ hour	2½ hours	3¼ hours
¾ hour	3 hours	3 ¾ hours
1 hour	1½ hours	2½ hours
1 hour	2 hours	3 hours
1 hour	2½ hours	3½ hours
1 hour	3 hours	4 hours
1½ hours	1½ hours	3 hours
1½ hours	2 hours	3½ hours
1½ hours	2½ hours	4 hours

To avoid setting up a nocturnal feeding pattern (see page 87), the maximum feeding interval during the day should ideally not exceed four hours.

If your baby was born prematurely, or if you're concerned about your baby's feeding patterns or weight gain, consult your doctor for specific recommendations.

A good guideline as to whether your baby is getting enough food is the number of wet nappies they produce in a day. While the number of bowel movements is also significant, this can vary as some babies soil every feed or daily, while others can go for up to 10 days. This is okay as long as your baby is producing wet nappies, is happy and contented, and is putting on weight.

If your baby isn't producing wet nappies every feed, then check with a health professional.

A Word on Inflexible Schedules

The newborn phase is about familiarising yourself with your baby's personality, emotional and physical needs — as well as understanding your own.

Your baby's emotional wellbeing in the first three months is much more important than establishing a schedule. Don't be in a rush to introduce, or be governed by, a timetable just because others are doing it. With a bit of give and take, a rhythm will naturally evolve through creating healthy sleeping and feeding patterns. Babies like consistency, but this does not mean they need stringent schedules. By all means use clocks to guide you, but try not to let them rule you. Babies have different thresholds and personalities and schedules do not take these into account.

Most importantly, try to relax and enjoy your baby. This time of your baby's life will never be repeated.

89

PART THREE
Feeding Your Baby

Feeding

Healthy eating habits begin from day one. Many hours are spent feeding, offering a unique opportunity for intimacy and nurturing.

- Feed in a calm environment.
- The less fuss around feed time, the better.
- Babies wake and want feeding immediately.
- Avoid waking a sleeping baby to feed during the night unless advised to do so by your medical professional.

Choose a quiet place to feed so you and your baby can relax and focus. A newborn's senses are acute, and constant chatter and household noise can be distracting and overstimulating. A calm baby will suck better, digest well, settle more easily and sleep soundly. This is especially important in the first six weeks.

Babies waking from a nap are more interested in food than a nappy change; it's the adults who worry about the nappy.

Babies wake and want feeding immediately. Many parents are taught to change a baby's nappy first. However, I have found that in the time it takes to change a nappy, a hungry baby can quickly progress from irritable to hysterical, then lack energy to focus and suck well. As a result, the mother becomes fraught, the baby picks up on the tension and reacts, adding to the mother's stress, and the unfortunate outcome is a hungry, dissatisfied baby and an unhappy, depleted mother.

A good option is to change the nappy halfway through feeding, which helps with gas release and encourages a baby to remain focused so they feed well.

Different Feeds and Feeding Rhythms

Different feeds can be described according to their time of day. There is no set way to feed a baby, however below are some of the more common feeding

rhythms you might like to try. As a rule of thumb, feed for hunger and not comfort. Some babies do need a top-up before going for their nap and this is okay — listen to your baby; this is not about feeding a baby to sleep, but ensuring your baby has a full tummy before going to bed.

Daytime Feeds

These are 'social feeds' as they fall within social hours for both mother and baby and involve 'socialising'. As your baby grows, cuddle time will combine with floor time.

- Feed
- Burp and change the nappy
- Finish feeding
- Cuddles and/or floor time
- Return to bed

or ...

- Feed
- Burp
- Finish feeding
- Change nappy and burp
- Cuddles and/or floor time
- Return to bed

or ...

- Full feed without breaks
- Burp and change nappy
- Cuddle and/or floor time
- Return to bed.

Last Feed of the Day

The last daytime feed normally occurs between 4 and 6 p.m. and incorporates bath time. Many babies sleep their longest stretch between the final feed of the day and when they naturally wake for their first night feed. The rhythm is:

- Full feed
- Burp
- Place baby safely on the floor nappy-free while running the bath
- Bath
- Dry and dress your baby
- Top-up feed
- Burp
- Return to bed.

Night Feeds

These feeds should be baby-led and not involve waking a sleeping baby. Night feeds should be prompted by your baby waking you — not by you waking them. In my opinion, if your baby is putting on weight, and is feeding well and regularly throughout the day, there is no need to wake them during the night to feed unless you have been advised by your medical practitioner to do so.

When your baby cries in the night, it is worth taking a moment to assess whether they are crying for food or for comfort. Sometimes they cry for a few moments then fall back to sleep. It is common for babies to wake themselves up at night with their startle reflex, especially if they are not swaddled, or while weeing, pooing, passing wind or merely 'fluffing up their pillows', so to speak. Often they can be easily resettled without feeding.

Try to resettle them initially but if it's clearly not working, then by all means feed, as a hungry baby will not resettle.

When it comes to resettling at night, it is not about *not* feeding your baby (a hungry baby will *not* resettle), but ensuring that if you do feed, that it is for hunger and not comfort.

Night feeds should always be carried out with the same focus and attention as daytime feeds, equal in both quantity and length of time.

Cutting corners by giving water or watered-down feeds as a substitute for breast milk or formula, or by shortening the feed, often results in an unsettled night with poor resettling and frequent waking.

Think of night feeds as 'business' or 'anti-social' feeds in the sense that you are there to do business and not to socialise. By keeping stimulation to a minimum your baby will resettle more easily. Engaging with them gives them a reason to want to stay awake. This is also a chance to reinforce the concept that night-time is ideally for sleeping.

95

Always feed in adequate lighting so that you can check that your baby is sucking well. It will also help your baby to focus and be less inclined to drift off.

Two variations for night feeding rhythms are:

• Full feed
• Burp and change nappy
• Offer breast again as a top-up
• Swaddle and return to bed

or ...

• Feed
• Burp and change nappy
• Finish feed
• Swaddle and return to bed.

Dream Feeds

Dream feeds are controversial — for good reason. Dream feeds are those given between 10 p.m. and midnight and differ from night feeds in that they involve picking up a sleeping baby for feeding, as opposed to responding to a baby who wakes naturally to feed. They are parent-led — the choice of the parent — not baby-led.

In my opinion it's important to weigh up the pros and cons before adding dream feeds to your feeding rhythm.

Research shows that dream feeds interfere with a baby's most precious and deepest phase of sleep that occurs in the hours leading up to midnight and that feeding during these hours can meddle with digestion, growth and development and can affect long-term sleeping patterns.

It is common for parents to introduce dream feeds in the hope that their baby will sleep for longer. However, there is no evidence to indicate that dream feeds guarantee parents extended sleep, nor benefit a healthy baby at all. In my opinion, dream feeds tend to be a quick fix and often create problems as your baby grows.

Make sure you are well informed as, once in place, dream feeds are difficult to eliminate from your baby's routine. If you are certain that dream feeds will work for you and your baby, ideally aim to stop them by the age of six months.

Burping

All babies, whether breast or bottle-fed, need burping. Effective burping techniques play a significant role in creating a contented baby.

- Burping is a technique that requires firm pressure and focus.
- A well-burped baby is likely to feed well, digest well and settle more easily.
- Often choosing a combination of burping techniques is required to release stubborn wind.
- All up, burping takes around five minutes.
- Some babies are more difficult to burp than others.

Bottle Analogy — Straight and Curved

Think of a bottle with bubbles in it; lay it down then stand it up — the bubbles come to the top. With this in mind, picture a bottle that is curved like a banana and imagine trying to move the bubbles from the bottom upwards, around the curve to the top. It's tricky to navigate the bend.

It is the same for your baby during burping — it helps if your baby's back remains as straight as possible so the gas can work its way out.

Burping Techniques

Sometimes stubborn wind requires a combination of the following burping techniques.

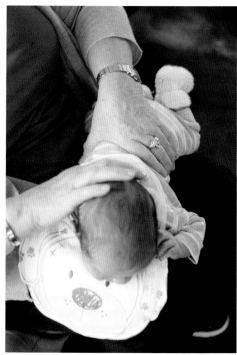 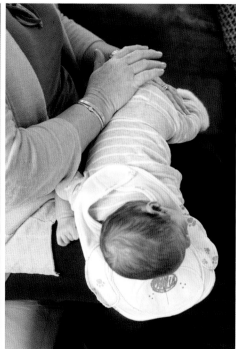

Over the Knees, Tummy Down

1. Place your baby over your knees facing tummy down, their left side farthest from you.
2. Support your baby's upper body by placing one hand across the shoulder blades.
3. With your other hand, reach across and slip your cupped hand under the side of your baby's body, and start rhythmically cupping up and down the tummy area. Initially, you may hear a sloshing noise that will disappear once the gas releases.
4. Next, span your baby's back so that your fingers reach one side and your thumb the other.
5. Starting from the top of their nappy line, apply a little pressure as you gently but firmly start rubbing up and down.
6. Support your baby by placing one hand on your baby's upper legs.
7. With your other hand, place your palm at the top of their nappy line and knead downwards over their bottom — left buttock, right buttock and centre — in three separate movements.

99

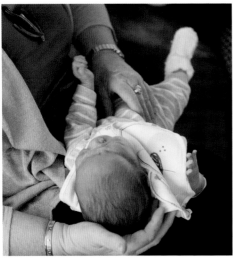 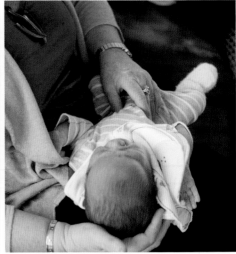

Over Your Knee on Their Back

1. Turn your baby onto their back and lay them flat so their head rests on one of your thighs.
2. Place one hand on your baby's chest for support.
3. With your other hand, span your baby's tummy and, using a kneading technique, massage the tummy inwards and outwards.
4. Using flat fingers or your fist, massage the tummy, ideally clockwise.

Tongue Position

Your baby's tongue should be at the base of the mouth to allow wind to pass. To check, place your baby in a seated position on your knee and hook your index finger on their chin and pull down on the lower jaw to open the mouth. Hopefully, the tongue will flop down. If it doesn't, try 'popping' the cheeks by gently pressing together your thumb and forefinger in the hollow at the base of your baby's cheeks.

Sitting Up Straight

Sit your baby on your knees facing towards you, your hands supporting them under their armpits. With a backward rotation, straighten out your baby's body so they are upright (babies with wind are often curled up) while applying a little pressure with your fingers to your baby's back.

Jiggle (bounce) your baby up and down on your knee. This can be fun for both of you as well as helping gas release.

On the Shoulder

1. Place your baby on your shoulder, facing towards you so that their chin is resting on the crest of your shoulder.
2. Using both hands, slip your thumbs under your baby's hips and tilt upwards in a backward rotation to straighten out the body. This may mean you need to lift them slightly away from your body. You must not pull their legs in an effort to straighten them, as this can dislocate their hips.
3. Using the same arm as the shoulder they are resting on, hook your forearm around and under their buttocks to support them.
4. With your other hand slightly cupped, span your baby's back so that your fingers reach one side and your thumb the other and, starting from the top of their nappy line, apply a little pressure as you gently but firmly start rubbing up and down.
5. Next, rub up one side, then the other, then with a cupped hand, pat all over your baby's back and sides.

With practice, a combination of these techniques will take no longer than five minutes to help release the gas from your baby's tummy.

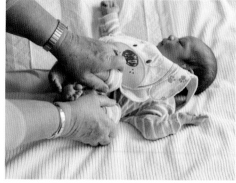
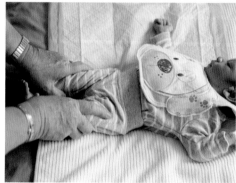
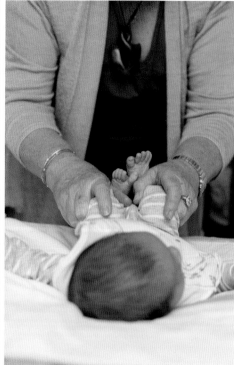

On the Change Table

1. Place your baby on the change table and gently but firmly take hold of your baby's legs just on, or below, the knees.
2. Keeping your baby's knees together, gently bend them and press so that the upper thighs rest on your baby's tummy.
3. Release slightly and with knees still bent, place to the left side of the tummy, gently press, then return to centre. Keeping knees bent, place to the right side of the tummy, gently press, then release fully so that legs are straight.
4. Repeat this sequence three times.

Nappy Change

The nappy change is a good opportunity for your baby to kick and stretch out and often helps gas release.

While these methods are a good starting point, you may find other techniques that work just as well or better for your baby.

103

The Art of Breastfeeding

There are many different ways to breastfeed a baby; it is about listening to your body and your baby's needs. As your baby grows, it is likely that your breastfeeding rhythm will change many times.

It takes a minimum of six weeks to fully establish breastfeeding and for some it takes longer as hormones and milk supply stabilise, and mother and baby learn the ropes.

While you and your baby are working together to master your technique, it's likely you will go through a kaleidoscope of emotions, swinging from one extreme to another. This is all very normal and, once you are aware of this, many find it easier to sit back and take it day by day with less expectation.

Some mothers find breastfeeding straightforward while others have to work at it. Some are overjoyed at taking on the role of breastfeeding their baby, others have mixed feelings, and for some it is not physically possible.

Whatever your situation, try not to judge yourself or measure your outcome against anyone else's. Breastfeeding is very personal. Try to fully embrace how you feel and have the confidence to go forward.

If you are having difficulty, don't hesitate to ask for help. Not everyone takes easily to the commitment of breastfeeding. Many mothers struggle and the key here is to reach out.

It is difficult to predict what your experience will be as all mothers and all babies respond differently.

What is Breast Milk?

Breast milk is the liquid produced by a mother as a response to pregnancy, birth and the sucking of the baby at the breast.

It is made up of water, protein, fats and milk sugar (lactose), carbohydrates, vitamins, minerals and other nutrients, including antibodies, enzymes and hormones. This composition is not constant; it differs from mother to mother, changes throughout the day and also as the baby grows, to accommodate its needs.

For mothers, having confidence they will be able to produce sufficient milk for their baby from birth is the first step. This is reinforced by the mother's positive thought processes throughout this time.

Oxytocin, the hormone responsible for the let-down reflex, is released in large amounts during childbirth and continues to be produced as a result of the stimulation of the nipples when the baby is put to the breast.

Oxytocin can be produced purely by the sound of a baby crying, or by putting the baby to your breast to suck. Another hormone, prolactin, is responsible for milk production, ensuring there is sufficient volume for each feed.

The baby uses its tongue and jaw to compress the breast tissue, squeezing the milk out. Then the magic happens: we have milk.

There are three different types of milk produced:

- colostrum
- transitional milk
- mature milk.

107

Colostrum

Colostrum is the first milk that is produced at the end of pregnancy and during the first few days after birth. Easily digested by newborns, colostrum is high in protein, low in fat and has a high concentration of antibodies to help fight off infections. It is also a natural laxative that helps clear the baby's body of meconium, the first thick, black, tarry stool.

The volume of colostrum is small but contains everything a new baby needs in the first few days of life.

It is quite normal for breastfed babies to lose up to 10 percent of their birth weight following birth, and it can take as long as two to three weeks to regain it.

Transitional Milk

Transitional milk is a combination of colostrum and mature milk. When your milk begins to come in at approximately three to five days after birth it mixes with the colostrum and gradually transitions to mature milk over the course of a few days or a week. For some mothers this can take longer. There is not a marked definition while feeding as to when colostrum ends and mature milk begins, but the process is complete by the time the baby is about two weeks old.

Mature Milk

Mature milk is a combination of foremilk and hind milk. Foremilk is thin, watery and lower in fat and calories. Hind milk is thicker, creamier and higher in fat and calories. There is no special moment when foremilk becomes hind milk.

The mixture of foremilk and hind milk differs for every mother and every baby. However, generally speaking, as the baby sucks from the breast and the feed progresses, the fat content of the milk rises and the volume decreases. The length of time between feeds can also affect milk composition.

Foremilk is high in volume and low in fat as opposed to hind milk, which is low in volume and high in fat, and it would appear that babies' needs dictate that foremilk is produced in abundance in hotter climates while hind milk is more abundant in cooler climates.

The colour of breast milk may vary throughout the day, or from one day to the next, often depending on what you eat or drink. This is perfectly normal.

Let-down Reflex

When your baby suckles, messages are sent to your brain, triggering the pituitary gland to release the hormones oxytocin and prolactin. Oxytocin causes contraction of the milk glands, squeezing the milk out into the milk ducts, while prolactin stimulates milk production. This is known as the 'let-down reflex'.

Feeding colostrum should take no longer than a few minutes on each breast. Feeding short and often is preferable to long and sometimes unproductive periods of sucking. In the first few days it is not uncommon for a mother to breastfeed anywhere between eight and 12 plus times a day.

108

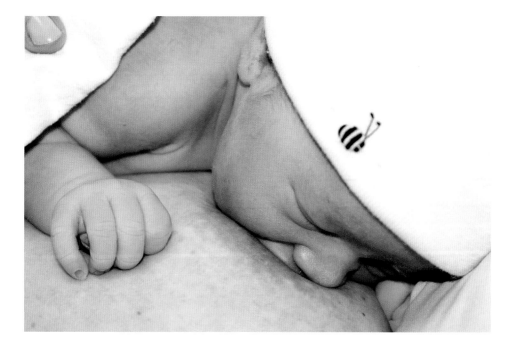

Establishing Breastfeeding

Breastfeeding comes down to good attachment, or a 'deep latch-on'. It is a precise technique that can make or break breastfeeding.

The shape and size of breasts can vary. Whether you have small or large breasts, it doesn't matter because milk is produced in deeply buried glands, not in the surrounding fatty tissue.

Likewise, the size and shape of nipples can vary. They can be small or large, naturally inverted or protruding , fat, squashed or cherry shaped, dark or pale, nobbly or hairy. Often they are not identical.

109

Good attachment:
- prevents nipple damage
- ensures good milk flow
- cuts down your baby's intake of air during feeding and the likelihood of intestinal discomfort.

Poor attachment may lead to:
- inefficient feeding
- sore, cracked or bleeding nipples
- blocked ducts
- mastitis.

Incorrect posture, posterior tongue-tied, poor latching on or a baby sucking on empty breasts are the most common causes of nipple issues. One of the reasons why so many mothers give up breastfeeding prematurely is that they cannot deal with the pain of cracked or bleeding nipples.

Nipple Shields

A nipple shield is a thin and flexible cover that is usually made from silicone, latex or rubber and placed over the nipple and areola during breastfeeding. It looks like a mini sombrero, although some have a portion of the border cut out so that the baby's nose is touching your breast rather than the shield. Nipple shields also come in different sizes and it is important to ensure you have the correct size for your nipples.

Some experts are in favour of nipple shields while others are not. In my opinion, it is better to breastfeed using nipple shields than to not breastfeed at all.

How to Use Nipple Shields

- Rinse the nipple shield with warm water to soften it and make it more pliable and to give a better seal (moistening the inside of the shield with breast milk also helps create suction).
- Stretch the shield slightly and place over your nipple, gently pressing the brim (flat part) to your skin so a seal forms.
- Another way of doing it is to turn the shield partially inside out (halfway or so), press in the tip of the shield (to increase suction) and place it over your nipple. Turn back the brim of the shield and gently press it on to your skin to create a seal. Pop out the tip — your nipple should be inside the tip of the shield.

Some mothers find that once the nipple shield is in place, hand expressing some breast milk into the shield can help get your baby started. Gently stroke your baby's lips with the tip of the shield so that their mouth opens as wide as possible. Do a deep latch-on by latching your baby on to the brim of the nipple shield — not just the tip. Be sure your baby is sucking.

Nipple shields tend to slow your baby's intake, which may mean that feeds take longer. Some mothers find that silicone shields are the easiest to use — see

One of the reasons why so many mothers give up breastfeeding prematurely is that they cannot deal with the pain of cracked or bleeding nipples.

which best suits you. While some experts believe that shields can lead to a decrease in milk supply, I believe that if used as temporary measure, they can actually help milk supply.

Nipple Shield Care
- Sterilise after use.
- Check for tears, cuts and cracks to the shield which can harbour bacteria. Replace if ever in doubt.
- Replace your nipple shields every month.
- Some mothers find it helpful to store shields on top of a sterilised dummy or teat so they can find them easily or store them in the container they come with as most shields are transparent.

111

A Deep Latch-on Technique

A deep latch-on helps your baby to empty your breasts more efficiently. It stimulates milk production, helps avoid nipple issues and reduces the intake of air as it provides a tighter latch or attachment.

With this technique you are effectively making available the most breast tissue possible; this will help your nipple to be correctly positioned inside your baby's mouth.

Different Holds

It is the baby's lower chin that milks the breasts and using a combination of the following two holds can help reduce breastfeeding issues:
- The half-cradle or Madonna hold
- The rugby or football hold.

The Half-cradle or Madonna Hold

If you choose to start feeding with your right breast, follow this sequence:

1. With your left arm, hold your baby so that your forearm supports along the length of their spine and your palm is gently cradling their head.
2. To do a deep latch-on, slide your right hand along your ribcage to the base of your right breast, slightly turning your hand out to cup your right breast at the base of the breast.
3. Imagine your breast as the face of a clock, and position your index finger at 3 o'clock and your thumb at 9 o'clock, and hold it in a U shape or how you would hold a sandwich. This should be a comfortable hold, so you may need to adapt to your body type.
4. Remember to keep your index finger and thumb at the base of your breast and firm against your rib cage and not let them move up towards the nipple, otherwise this will interfere with your baby's lower jaw as it latches on to the breast.
5. Line your baby up so that your nipple is midway between the bottom of your baby's nose and top lip.
6. Squeeze your breast with the amount of tension you would when holding a salad sandwich so that your nipple and surrounding tissue protrude — it is less of a pinching action and more of a pressing action, but be gentle.
7. Bring your baby to your breast, not breast to baby.
8. For some it takes practice to do this well — try to be patient.

If the U-shape technique feels uncomfortable or seems difficult, adjust the positioning so that it's more comfortable. It is vital you apply enough pressure so that the nipple and breast protrude for a better latch-on.

Many mothers use a pillow to support the baby, which helps maintain a more upright posture for the mother (see opposite).

The Rugby or Football Hold

For a rugby or football hold, tuck your baby under your arm so that the soles of their feet point behind you.

1. Use a pillow to support your baby from underneath and tuck your baby under your arm.
2. Cradle your baby's head in your palm.
3. Using the opposite hand to the breast — for example, left breast, right hand — hold it in a C-shape with your forefinger and thumb at the 12 and 6 o'clock positions.
4. Squeeze your breast so that the nipple and breast tissue protrude for latching on.
5. Bring baby to breast (see above).

How to Remove Your Baby from the Breast

The easiest way to break the attachment is to gently press down with the tip of your forefinger onto your breast close to your baby's mouth to release the suction. Slip your middle finger into your baby's mouth. While some babies release easily, others form a tight latch that is more difficult to break.

When talking about breastfeeding, mothers tend to talk about the time spent on the breast. Remember, it's not the time that your baby spends on the breast, but the actual productive sucking.

113

Often a baby who wants to suck constantly is not necessarily hungry but is sucking for comfort. In these cases, try offering a dummy/pacifier to give your nipples a rest. Some mothers are informed that sucking on a dummy/pacifier or offering a bottle causes nipple confusion, however, in my experience, this is not an issue. Most babies spend time in the womb sucking their thumb and a dummy/pacifier is simply an extension of this.

Supply — When Your Milk Comes In

Milk usually arrives between days three and five; however, I have found that it can come in as early as day one.

You will know when your milk comes in. Breasts can become large, full and rock-hard, and can be tender, sore and uncomfortable. Some breasts become lumpy. Many mothers go to bed with empty breasts and wake a few hours later with them full. For others, it happens during the day. *All of this is normal.*

In these early days, to establish your milk supply ideally you will feed by alternating sides and using different holds to stimulate your milk supply, thus protecting your nipples from being damaged. Until such time as feeding settles down, I encourage mothers to feed from both sides, alternating both the Madonna and football holds.

Once Supply is Established

114

Once your milk supply settles down, how you offer the breast is your choice and will depend on the needs of both you and your baby.

One option is to offer one breast per feed. This is often recommended as it enables your baby to get as much hind milk as possible by fully emptying each breast. When feeding this way, I suggest doing both the Madonna and football hold during the feed.

Another option is to feed for equal amounts of time on each breast. Some believe that this does not empty the breasts fully and therefore the baby does not get as much hind milk as a baby who feeds from the one side only.

The 'Cake and Icing'

If it seems your baby is not fully satisfied when feeding from one breast, it is worth trying the following. Give the main feed from the side that you start with, then change to the second breast for a few minutes, then return to the

first side to 'empty' the breast. I call this 'taking the cake from the first and the icing from the second'.

What is Cluster Feeding?

Cluster feeding involves feeding more frequently at the end of the day, perhaps two to three times within the space of as many hours. It can help an unsettled baby and also gives mothers an opportunity to put their feet up.

How Do You Know When Your Baby Has Finished?

Unfortunately, you don't — this is the gamble of breastfeeding. It differs from baby to baby, however, it is important to emphasise that it is not the length of time that your baby sucks, but whether your baby is sucking productively.

Common Breastfeeding Issues

While the following breastfeeding issues are not insurmountable, they can be a challenge and alter your experience considerably. In some cases, mothers facing nipple and breast issues choose to discontinue breastfeeding prematurely yet, in my opinion, many of these issues can be avoided if correct guidance is given from day one. It is a good idea to check your breasts regularly for signs of change.

*To remember which side to begin on,
wear either a breastfeeding bracelet or
a ribbon. (For more on keeping records,
see page 86.)*

Cracked Nipples
- Ensure you have a good latch-on.
- Check baby's tongue for posterior tongue-tie.
- Apply breastmilk to nipple to help heal — massage it in after feeds and allow to air dry.
- Apply cream or ointment — several are available so work out which works best for you.
- Air your nipples as much as possible. Fresh air helps healing.
- Breast shells are great — while you may look like Wonder Woman they help keep the air circulating while you are fully dressed.

Engorgement
Engorgement can occur around days three to five when the milk comes in.

Because it's the baby's lower chin that helps milk the breasts, varying the feeding positions can help ease engorgement. In particular, the rugby hold (football) helps relieve pressure under the armpits.

To ease discomfort, try warm compresses before feeds, and massage before feeding and during feeding (warmth helps milk flow; cold stops milk flow).

After feeding, cold compresses or cabbage leaves tucked in the bra for a few minutes can help (see below).

Blisters, aka Blebs
Blisters, also called blebs, can be painful. Some mothers get blisters in the first few days in response to poor attachment. To relieve the pain, the blister needs to be punctured.

Occasionally, a blocked duct or mastitis can be associated with a blister on the nipple. However, it is possible to develop a blister without experiencing a blocked duct or mastitis.

Blocked Ducts

A blocked duct is not thought to be an infection and therefore does not require treatment with antibiotics. Often they can be easily resolved by continuing to breastfeed. It is likely that the flow will be slower on the side with the blocked duct. When feeding, offer your baby the affected side first, as their strong sucking action will stimulate flow and help clear the duct. You can also try the following:

- Use a compress to apply heat to the affected area.
- Make sure you do a good deep latch-on technique — this is crucial.
- Often it helps if your baby is positioned in such a way that the chin points directly to the blocked duct.
- During feeding, massage your breast or do compression techniques.

Mastitis

Mastitis is often due to a bacterial infection. Bacteria can enter the breast through a crack in the nipple. Symptoms include a painful lump in the breast, redness and pain of the breast, fever and flu-like symptoms.

Mastitis may also be caused by milk staying in the breast — 'milk stasis'.

- As with blocked ducts, apply heat to the affected area.
- Ensure you have a good, deep latch-on technique.
- Feed your baby positioned so that the chin points directly to the blocked duct.
- During feeding, massage your breast or do compression techniques.

Compresses

Compresses can be either hot, for encouraging milk flow, or cold for slowing down milk flow.

How to Make Cold Compresses

There are various ways to make a compress but this is a simple and effective option: dampen a disposable nappy and place it in the freezer.

Another alternative is to use commercial products that can be used cold or hot. Once frozen, allow it to thaw a little and wrap it around the breast. It will mould to the breast as it continues to thaw. Ideally, don't leave it on longer than 10–20 minutes maximum.

117

How to Make Hot Compresses

Wet a face cloth and place it in the microwave for a few seconds until it is very warm — alternatively wet it under the hot water tap. Test before placing on your breast. Mould the cloth around the breast. Ideally, leave on for no longer than a few minutes.

Cabbage Leaves

Cabbage leaves are thought to contain an enzyme that helps reduce swelling in cases of engorged breasts. Place a cabbage leaf directly onto your breast under your bra and leave on for no longer than 20 minutes (leaving for long periods can dry up your milk supply).

Raw Potatoes

In my experience, if used early, raw potatoes help take away the inflammation, redness and soreness. They need to be applied as soon as possible — ideally, in the first 24 hours. (If left longer, the infection will be too strong for it to work; in this case you will need antibiotics.)

1. Cut six to eight potatoes lengthwise, then into thin slices, and soak in a bowl of water for approximately 15 minutes.
2. Apply the potato slices to the affected area of the breast and leave on for 15 minutes.
3. Remove potatoes and throw away.
4. After another 15 minutes (approximately) repeat the procedure. Do this three times in total.

Supply Issues

Always believe and tell yourself out loud that you have milk! This will help stimulate the production of the hormones oxytocin and prolactin that are necessary for milk production.

Breast massage or breast compression can also help stimulate supply. Work with your baby, cupping your breast from underneath while feeding, with your thumb on one side and fingers to the other side, gently massaging downwards in sync with your baby's sucking motion.

Milking the breasts fully by varying the holds helps access different milk ducts.

How to Support and Maintain Your Milk Supply

The following tips can be useful to help support and maintain your milk supply:

- Eating sensibly — lots of good carbohydrate and protein meals, plus protein snacks
- Fenugreek — helps with milk supply
- Mothers' breastfeeding herbal teas — help with milk supply
- Natal vitamins[*]
- Omega 3[*] — boosts the fatty milk
- Pea Protein shakes or protein shakes, i.e. Complan or Tiger's milk
- Probiotics — can help with digestive issues for both mother and baby
- Water — a large percentage of breast milk is made up of water so it's a good idea to drink an extra 120 ml of water at feed time (think of it as your baby's feed)
- Medications from your doctor, e.g. Domperidon/Motilium.[*]

Supplementary Nursing System (SNS)

For mothers with supply issues who want to establish breastfeeding and have been recommended to do top-ups (with bottles), it it worth trying a supplementary nursing system (SNS), also known as Lact-Aid.

This is a kit that contains a bag and a tube system for feeding your baby additional milk while breastfeeding. By using the SNS system, your baby is able to suck on the breast, which in turns helps increase your milk supply, without the need for bottle-feeding, which can often lead to supply issues.

These kits are readily available online.

119

---

[*]   When taking these, check you do not exceed your folic acid requirement.

> **Breastfeeding and Skin-to-skin**
> If at any stage you have issues with breastfeeding,
> it's worth initiating skin-to-skin contact. Often
> your baby will start rooting and naturally
> latch on to your breast.

FAQs

The four most commonly asked questions relating to babies and breastfeeding are:
- Is my baby tongue-tied?
- What do I do if I suspect my baby is lactose intolerant?
- How do I deal with a sleepy baby during breastfeeding?
- How do I know if my baby is getting enough?

Is My Baby Tongue-tied?

What is tongue-tie? Ankyloglossia is the medical term given to those babies whose frenulum, the band of tissue connecting the base of the tongue to the floor of the mouth, is too short and tight, restricting movement of the tongue.

How to Tell if Your Baby is Tongue-tied

If your baby is unable to extend their tongue fully, or the tongue tip has a heart-shaped appearance, it is likely that your baby is tongue-tied. Sometimes this is accompanied by a clicking noise while feeding, or a habit of breaking suction throughout the feed. Mothers may experience nipple pain because the baby is chewing rather than sucking. Chewing can also lead to slow weight gain and affect milk supply.

Posterior tongue-tie often goes undetected. If you have nipple issues, consult an expert who specialises in tongue-tie to check for this. You may have to get it checked a few times as it is often missed during consultations.

Less common is upper lip tie (ULT) where the frenulum inside the upper lip may be short, affecting the baby's ability to latch on. Signs may include a clicking sound, the top lip rolling in, or frequent popping off the breast.

What to Do for a Tongue-tied Baby

If feeding is not affected, leave well alone. Ankyloglossia can often rectify itself. If it does affect feeding, have your baby checked by a health professional who

121

specialises in tongue-tie and upper lip tie to assess whether a simple corrective procedure is required.

What to Do if Your Baby is Lactose Intolerant

If your baby is lactose intolerant, it is still possible to breastfeed.

- Try modifying your diet by completely eliminating dairy from your diet, including food products that contain whey — read labels before you buy products and pre-packaged foods.
- Feed exclusively from one breast per feed so your baby gets as much hind milk as possible — this is easier on your baby's digestive system as it is lower in lactose than foremilk.
- Take supplements to increase your 'fatty' milk.
- Massage your breasts while your baby is feeding to encourage milk flow.
- If feeding both sides, it may help to first pump a little off the second breast before offering to your baby — this helps reduce the quantity of foremilk.

How to Deal with a Sleepy Baby during Breastfeeding

Many babies tend to nod off on the breast. Being nestled close to you where they feel safe and nurtured is often a signal for them to doze off.

It is not the length of time that the baby is attached to the breast, but the productive sucking time that guarantees that they are feeding. A baby that isn't sucking, isn't feeding.

If your baby falls asleep, they will not be sucking productively — therefore try detaching. This normally wakes them so you can then re-attach and resume feeding.

You may also choose to change the nappy at this point or offer the other breast, both of which help regain your baby's attention.

Feeding a Sleepy Baby

If your baby tends to fall asleep during feeding and is not gaining weight, the following guidelines will help you keep them awake to ensure they feed well and in turn have better weight gains. Throughout, be sure your baby is sucking more than 'stopping and starting'. A good way to encourage them to do this is to gently press with your thumb under their chin on their jawbone. If this doesn't work, remove them and re-attach.

- Baby wakes.
- Start on one side in a Madonna hold.
- Allow your baby to suck until they stop.
- Offer the other side until they stop.
- Offer the first side again in a football hold, allowing them to suck until they stop.
- Offer the second side again in a football hold — allowing them to suck until they stop.
- Change, burp, then re-offer the first side and repeat the cycle.

The goal is to ensure your baby empties the first side more fully than the second side.

You may wish to massage your breast while your baby is feeding to help bring down the hind milk. This whole cycle may take approximately 35 to 40 minutes, including burping and nappy change.

After feeding, swaddle your baby and return them to bed.

How Do You Know Your Baby is Getting Enough?
A happy and contented baby is the best indication. Other signs include:
- productive sucking
- wet nappies
- healthy sleep habits
- weight gains
- soiled nappies.

Combining Breastfeeding and Supplementary Feeding (Expressed Milk or Formula)
Mixed feeding, or supplementing breastfeeding with formula, is a grey area as many mothers are unaware of how it interferes with breastfeeding, especially in the first three months.

The First Few Days
In my experience, giving your newborn a one-off bottle of formula while waiting for your milk to come in will not ruin your chances of breastfeeding. Often this appeases a tired mother and baby who haven't yet had a decent night's sleep. Once rested, the chances of successful breastfeeding increase tenfold.

123

Keep in mind that a newborn baby's cry in the first few days is not necessarily a sign of hunger; more often than not they want comfort sucking, or to be held. Most babies have taken sufficient nourishment from the placenta pre-birth to get them through the first few days on colostrum only. If your baby is crying excessively, try holding them or offer a dummy/pacifier.

Once your milk comes in, however, it's best for both of you to put aside any form of supplementary feeding so that your baby can begin focusing on feeding from the breast.

Mixed Formula and Breastfeeding in the First Six Weeks

On the whole 'mixed feeding' is not something I encourage, unless the baby needs it. While I believe it is every mother's right to choose how they feed, it is helpful to know that breastfeeding is a process governed by a complex hormonal system, in which your baby's sucking ability plays a key role in stimulating milk supply.

When your baby sucks, messages are sent to your brain to release hormones that stimulate milk production. Therefore, if your baby sucks on a teat instead of your breast, your body produces less milk. This is nature's law of supply and demand at work.

When thinking about topping up with a bottle after a feed, it is important to understand that this can lead to a fall in your milk production. In my experience, it is possible to top up by re-offering the breast 15 minutes before a nap or bed time. To avoid a feed-sleep association, feed then swaddle before putting your baby in their bed. (FSS — feed, swaddle, sleep). For those who do not swaddle their babies, choose another activity to do in its place to break the feed-sleep association.

For those who feed their baby while swaddled, it's a good idea that when the top up is finished, to unswaddle them and re-swaddle them, before sleep.

Some babies take to the bottle well and then become lazy on the breast, refusing to attach and suck properly, waiting instead for the bottle. This can also lead to supply issues.

Some parents are told that giving a bottle of formula makes the baby sleep better at night. This is not true for all babies. Also it is important to realise that, when breastfeeding, the night feeds play a role in stimulating milk supply, facilitating better feeding, especially in the early weeks.

Sharing the Feeding — Is It a Good Idea?

Before you make your decision, be aware that introducing a bottle for the sake of freeing up time doesn't always work out as planned. For example, it is usually the mother who intuitively wakes in the night, often before the baby cries, while the partner continues to sleep through a newborn's cry. The mother wakes her partner and often remains awake throughout.

Furthermore, skipping a breastfeed is not so straightforward; most mothers have to get out of bed at this point to express in order to relieve full breasts.

The best way that your family and friends can support you is by giving you a chance to rest while your baby rests so that you feel refreshed and energised when your baby naturally wakes to feed.

In my experience, involving your partner or family in the feeding is more likely to work if you wait until after the initial 12 weeks, unless you need support beforehand.

Once your partner or co-feeder becomes involved in feeding, choose a time of the day that your partner or co-feeder is available, and keep it consistent. Try not to miss a day. What tends to work best is the evening or last feed of the day that includes bath time, or the night feed. Or you may wish to offer your baby the breast, followed by a bath then have your co-feeder or partner introduce the bottle. If your baby refuses the bottle, try it the other way: bottle, bath, followed by breast.

125

Refusing the Bottle

Some breastfed babies find it difficult to learn how to drink from a bottle. Latching on to a teat is a different technique to attaching to a breast.

Many mothers confess to having mixed feelings about introducing the bottle and often the baby can sense this. It helps if the mother is one hundred per cent sure — in a sense it gives the baby 'permission' to feed from the bottle.

Some experts advise that the mother should leave the room or house while a support person tries to feed the baby the bottle. In my experience, success is more likely if the mother remains present so the co-feeder can work with her to encourage the baby to take the bottle.

Try not to see it as a battle of wills! Do not force feed. There is a fine line between encouraging and forcing.

Positioning during Bottle-feeding

Feed at the same angle as if your baby were on your breast.

Breast milk squirts out via numerous holes, which differs from formula emptying from a bottle via a single hole. Therefore, contrary to what most people assume, it is important to maintain a certain level of pace. Choosing a suitable teat is important so your baby doesn't get frustrated.

Try to find a teat that is similar to your nipple in shape, i.e. short versus long.

In my experience, I often have success with a basic teat, or a latex teat, over a more elaborate version. See what works best for you.

Remember it is the baby's lower jaw that milks a breast, therefore placing the teat on your baby's lower lip (rather than the centre of the mouth) will encourage your baby to suck.

Some babies refuse the bottle outright and cannot be coaxed, even with a bottle of expressed milk. If your baby is clearly not willing to take it initially, put it away and try reintroducing it again in a few days' time.

Top-up Feeds before Naps

Generally speaking, the majority of breastfed babies in the first six weeks will feed once during a waking interval. However, as your baby grows and is awake for longer, you may wish to offer a top-up feed or a second full feed before returning your baby to bed, to ensure that they go to bed well fed.

126

When to Add Top-ups and Extra Feeds

In my experience, babies between six and 12 weeks digest at different rates, and it is best to follow your baby's cues. For example, if your baby is not settling well, is always hungry, is a fast feeder, or increasingly needs feeding as a last resort to get them to sleep, try offering a top-up feed before settling.

What is the Best Age to Introduce a Bottle?

In my experince age doesn't seem to be a factor. Some babies as old as seven months who have known nothing but breast will happily take to the bottle or cup. I also know babies that have taken a bottle from time to time since they were six weeks old who later refuse it.

Expressing Milk

For mothers who know they are going to have a Caesarean or are aware of a medical issue at time of birth, it is recommended nowadays to start hand-expressing colostrum at around week 36. Always check with your lead maternity carer (LMC) midwife, consultant or doctor, or a lactation consultant, before doing this. Save your colostrum in syringes, mark with date and name, and freeze.

Hand Expressing
- Wash your hands.
- The ideal time to express is after a shower or bath as the heat will help the flow of the colostrum. Alternatively, a nice warm compress will have the same effect.
- Sit in a comfortable chair, leaning slightly forward (gravity helps the flow).
- You will need a sterilised container to express the milk into.
- Start with a gentle breast massage or stroking from the back of your breast downwards towards the nipple. Another way is to massage using full circular movements, starting from the back of the breast to the nipple.
- Place your little finger under your breast, against your ribs, at the same time spreading your other fingers to cup the breast. Your thumb needs to be on the top, adjusting your fingers and thumb opposite each other so they make a C shape around the breast. Your index finger and thumb will be on either side of the nipple, positioned at the edge of the areola. Feel for a change in texture from the softness of the nipple and areola and start expressing. (This position will differ from breast to breast and, if you have a large areola, you may need to place your fingers inside it.)
- Using the length of your finger and thumb (rather than just your fingertips) start expressing, being sure not to pinch or squeeze your nipple.
- Press gently inwards toward the rib cage.
- Gently but firmly squeeze your thumb and first finger together, then release, keeping your finger and thumb in the same position.
- Repeat the squeezing and releasing, building up a rhythm, and rotate all around the nipple. When the flow slows or stops, change breasts.
- Be patient — it takes time to learn this technique and for the colostrum to flow.
- Store it in the freezer until you need it.

127

Mechanical Pumping

In my experience, your baby is the best 'pump' so unless there are medical reasons, I encourage mothers to avoid pumping in the first six weeks.

Circumstances that may require expressing include:

- a premature baby
- a difficult birth where the baby is being cared for in a nursery
- failure to thrive, perhaps due to attachment issues
- a baby who refuses to suck from the breast
- a tongue-tied baby.

Some mothers are advised to pump to help relieve engorged breasts, blocked ducts or mastitis. However, in most circumstances, I encourage mothers to do this naturally by using the baby. In my opinion, your baby is always the better option when it comes to establishing milk supply, balancing hormones and clearing infection.

When using a pump, there is always the risk of taking off too much milk and upsetting supply. While some mothers respond to expressing well, many have difficulty, which often creates anxiety. Sadly, I have met several mothers in tears because they cannot express which in turn affects milk supply.

One of the reasons why expressing can be difficult is because oxytocin, the 'love' hormone, doesn't always kick in at the sight of a pump! Some mothers have found watching a slide show of their baby while expressing can trigger the necessary emotional response.

If it turns out that expressing is your best option, it is a good idea is to do so at a regular time each day to help regulate your supply. Alternatively, you may wish to pump off a little at the end of each feed so by the end of the day you have enough for a full feed. This way there is less chance of affecting supply and demand, which helps build milk supply.

Some mothers choose to pump so they can have their partner or co-feeder give a bottle of expressed milk during the night. If the mother is able to sleep through, this can work well.

For whatever reason you choose to give up breastfeeding, you can always re-lactate if you choose to. It does take time and patience but it can be done. However, I always encourage mothers to think it through before making changes that could affect the whole family.

Breast Pump Hygiene
The best advice is to follow the manufacturer's instructions.

'Tiger Milk' Smoothie
A time-honoured 'Tiger milk' smoothie can help your milk supply.
Combine in a blender:
600 ml milk
one egg
one scoop of Complan
one banana (or berries)
half a dessertspoon of brewer's yeast

This makes three glasses — a day's supply of this pick-me-up.

129

Bottle-feeding

Some mothers cannot breastfeed due to medical reasons. No matter how much they want to breastfeed nor how hard they try, it simply isn't physically possible.

Before we venture further I urge all mothers to put aside their breast-versus-bottle views and rally together in support of our mothers who were sadly not given the chance to choose.

Every mother has a right to be happy — we all know a happy mother makes for a happy baby and, ultimately, this is what counts. As with most aspects of parenting there is no right or wrong way — the 'best' way is what works best for the individual mother and baby.

Bottle-feeding offers as much opportunity for intimacy and nurturing as breastfeeding, especially in the first three months when a mother and baby are exploring each other and learning the ropes.

- Keep co-feeders to a minimum.
- Choose the right formula.
- Choose the right bottle and teats.
- Hygiene is crucial.
- Bottle-feeding is very much about making choices.

Co-feeders

Bottle-feeding should always be done respectfully with care and patience in a calm environment.

Ideally, limit co-feeders to three, including yourself, to create consistency. Handing a newborn around for bottle-feeding can be stressful and confusing for the baby. Giving time, one-to-one attention and being relaxed is what your baby wants — tender loving care (TLC), cuddles and knowing you have time for them.

Bottle-feeding requires your focus and presence. Don't be tempted to leave your baby alone with a bottle propped to save time — this can be dangerous and deprives your baby of the sense of security and bonding that comes with one-to-one feeding.

131

Formula

The world's first commercial infant formula was developed in 1867. Its creator was progressive German chemist Justus von Liebig who is credited with inventing nitrogen-based fertiliser and the Oxo bouillon cube.

Choosing Formula

For 150 years experts have continued to analyse breast milk, striving to mimic its composition. With so many types of formula available, it is important to do your research ahead of time. Formula should always be prepared according to the manufacturer's instructions.

Types of Formula

Although the composition of infant formula is constantly evolving, the following types are readily available.

Dairy-based Formula

Consists of different combinations of whey and casein and is easily available over the counter:

- lactose-free formula — does not contain the milk sugar called lactose
- organic dairy-based formula — free of chemicals and pesticides
- partially hydrolysed formula — this is designed to be more easily digested
- hydrolysed formula — a specialised formula, available through medical professionals.

Non–dairy Formula

The following dairy-free alternatives are available:

- goat's milk formula
- soya-based formula.

Changing Formula

My motto is: you can't change your baby's formula like you would your underwear.

Newborns' digestive systems are too sensitive to be constantly changing formula. Ideally, choose one and stick with it. If your baby reacts adversely to the brand you are using, by all means try an alternative. In other words, it should be a baby-led decision. As a guideline, 10 days is a reasonable timeframe for testing if a new formula is suitable.

Choosing Bottles

Plastic versus Glass

It is important to fully research before deciding whether you use plastic or glass bottles. Nowadays, it is thought that bottles made of BPA-free plastic bottles are safer than the old-fashioned plastic, however, as more research results are published, there are still concerns about the safety of using plastics with babies. If you have toddlers and choose to use glass bottles, you may wish to consider the safety aspects. For example, glass bottles are heavier than plastic and become warmer to the touch after heating. You may wish to buy sleeves to insulate the glass.

132

Recycling Bottles

Reusing old bottles depends on the condition of the bottle. Always opt for BPA-free plastic bottles and look for scratches and other signs of degeneration.

Bottle Shape

Various shapes promise improved digestion. For example, some contain funnel inserts that are thought to aid gas issues, and many advertise anti-colic properties. Disposable liners that fit into a hard plastic outer are also available.

Choosing a Teat

Teats come in various sizes and shapes and choosing one can be a process of trial and error. Modern teats are made of silicone, latex or rubber. Silicone is the most commonly used, although rubber is the most natural.

Evolution of Formula

In the early 1900s, mothers were recommended to blend untreated cow's milk, water, cream and sugar to feed their newborns. When cases of rickets, scurvy and bacterial infections emerged, orange juice and cod liver oil were added.

Between the 1920s and 1950s, evaporated milk was the most common component of infant formula.

Milk Flow and Hole Size

Perhaps the most important feature is the size of the hole, which influences milk flow and your baby's ability to suck and swallow.

Teats are graded as slow, medium or fast, according to the size of the hole — a smaller hole gives a slower flow and a large one a faster flow. During feeding, be attentive to gauge whether or not the teat shape or hole size is suitable.

If your baby guzzles, gags or the milk is running down your baby's cheek, the flow is likely to be too fast and a slower teat is needed. Also check the angle of the bottle during feeding as this also affects the flow.

If your baby is clearly tired from sucking and you can see that very little milk has been consumed, then this is a good indication that the hole is too small.

Some teats and bottles can be interchangeable but in general it is best to match the bottle and teat of the same brand to avoid ill-fitting seals and spillages.

The How-to of Bottle-feeding

Preparing the Formula
- Boil the water in a kettle.
- Fill the bottle to required level and leave to cool.
- Add scoops of formula. For quantities, follow the manufacturer's exact instructions. It is important to adhere to these quantities as adding extra powder can cause constipation and dehydration issues, while economising can lead to poor nourishment.
- Put on the teat and cap and swirl or shake until the powder is dissolved. (If your baby has colic or reflux, swirl rather than shake the bottle to help reduce air bubbles.) A good way to check is to look at the base of the bottle for sediment, or rest and check for lumps floating to the top.
- Test the temperature of the formula on the inside of your wrist before feeding — it should match your body temperature.
- For hygiene reasons, avoid touching your wrist with the teat.

Giving a Bottle
Let your newborn snuggle into your body or breast while feeding. This makes it possible to provide warmth and nurturing, making it a pleasurable experience for both of you.
- Position your baby so their body is straight and lying at a 45-degree angle. Your baby ideally should not be sitting up — 45 degrees is not a seated position.
- For stability and comfort, hold the bottle just below the teat.
- Make sure the teat goes on top of your baby's tongue, not under.
- Insert as much of the teat as possible into your baby's mouth — not just the tip.

As a guideline, it takes around 20 minutes to feed a bottle. However, every baby feeds differently and it's okay to split the feeds into two or three parts. For instance, your feeding rhythm may be:
- full bottle, burp, nappy change

- half bottle, nappy change, burp, second half of bottle, burp
- a third of the bottle, burp, second third of the bottle, change, burp, final third of the bottle, burp.

Bottle-feeding and Top-ups

Generally speaking, bottle-fed babies don't need top-ups, however, it depends on how your baby feeds. If your baby is only taking a small amount at a time, or if your baby seems hungry or is not settling well, then it may it may be a good idea to offer a top-up feed 15 minutes before they go to bed.

To avoid a feed-sleep association, feed, then swaddle, before your putting baby in their bed — Feed, Swaddle, Sleep, or FSS. For those who do not swaddle their babies, choose another activity to do in its place to break the feed-sleep association.

For those who feed their baby while they are swaddled, it's a good idea once the top-up is finished to unswaddle them then re-swaddle before sleep.

The Sterilising Process

Sterilising the equipment properly after every use is vital to kill bacteria. Poor hygiene causes gastro-intestinal issues.

Pre-sterilising

- After feeding, rinse the bottles, teats and lids with cold water and leave to sit on the draining board or in a plastic container.
- Unscrew bases of bottles and remove nipples from lids. Using a bottlebrush, wash well with hot soapy water. When washing teats, be sure to squirt soapy water through the teat.
- Rinse well using hot running water. When rinsing teats, be sure to squirt running, clear water through the holes.
- Place articles into the steriliser with the wide opening facing downwards.

Sterilising Methods

Traditional

Boiling is an oldie but a goodie. Ideally, use a large dedicated pot, submerge the bottles, teats, and lids and boil on a high heat for 5–10 minutes with the lid on. There should be enough water so that the bottles are fully submerged to prevent air bubbles collecting in the bottles. Turn off and leave to cool. In some countries the items may discolour or develop a chalky coat, which is not believed to be harmful to babies.

Going electric — my personal choice
Electric sterilisers can be bulky and take up counter space. If you have limited space, a compact microwave steam steriliser is ideal. Always read the instructions before use.

On the move
Travel steam sterilisers are available in some countries and normally hold up to two bottles. Alternatively, microwave steam sterilising bags are convenient for travelling. The bags can be reused; check the manufacturer's instructions.

Dishwasher
If sterilising in the dishwasher, it is important to pre-rinse your dishes. Place your bottle-feeding equipment on the top shelf. Some of the newer dishwashers have special sanitising or sterilising functions.

Chemicals
This is a personal choice although I prefer not to use chemicals to sterilise equipment.

Optional Equipment for Bottle-feeding
Container for Dishwasher
This is an absolute must if using the dishwasher, otherwise the lids, teats and screw lids end up all over the place and fill up with water.

Bottle-drying Rack
This is a great piece of equipment if you want to air-dry your bottles after removing from the steriliser, dishwasher or pot.

Formula Containers

Another useful gadget is a formula powder container that is divided into segments, one segment per feed. They are especially useful when travelling or out for the day.

Bottle-warmer

Not essential. I rarely use a bottle-warmer as I find boiling a kettle is quicker and more efficient for heating a bottle, and I tend to feed formula at room temperature.

Dummy/Pacifier Hygiene

Keeping dummies/pacifiers clean helps avoid oral thrush in your baby.

- Wash and sterilise dummies/pacifiers after each use.
- Have two or more in rotation so that you can keep up to date with washing and sterilising after each use.
- Ideally, store clean dummies/pacifiers in a clean container.
- Replace your dummies/pacifiers every six to eight weeks — to test a dummy/pacifier, press the bulb and if it remains stuck together, it needs replacing.
- Resist the temptation to clean dummies/pacifiers with your own saliva.
- Never put anything on a dummy/pacifier, such as honey.

137

Colic and Reflux

Reflux and colic are common in young babies because their digestive systems are still developing.

Spitting Up, Spilling, Puking, Chucking, Throwing Up or Regurgitation
Many healthy babies hiccup, cough or regurgitate milk after feeding. These are considered minor symptoms — there is no need for concern provided your baby is gaining weight and is content.

The Happy Spiller
Happy spillers regurgitate milk numerous times a day or may vomit once or twice, then are happy and contented. (Spills smell like milk, vomit has a more rancid odour.) It may be a small amount of milk that reappears almost as soon as it's gone down or it may come up later as partly digested or curdled milk. At times there may be a dramatic gush from both the nose and mouth.

Spilling affects both breast-fed and formula-fed babies and improves with age as your baby's digestive tract matures. It may begin soon after birth, or it might not start for three months. Some babies go through phases of frequent vomiting that suddenly, for no apparent reason, stop.

Some happy spillers continue to spit up into toddler years. While this can be inconvenient and distressing for a parent, it is not harmful to the baby and is not considered a form of reflux.

The Unhappy Spiller

An unhappy spiller is a term describing a 'reflux baby', suffering from gastro-oesophageal reflux (GOR), also spelt gastro-esophageal reflux (GER). This is the medical term given to stomach acid and milk rising upwards out of the stomach into the oesophagus and mouth.

In young babies the sphincter muscle or valve that separates the stomach and oesophagus is weak and the undigested contents easily escape upwards. As babies grow, this muscle tightens and reflux becomes less common. Reflux is unpredictable and some days will be better than others. It is thought that reflux babies experience heartburn symptoms, which cause discomfort and distress. Symptoms will be similar to those of the happy spiller, but with vivid signs of distress.

Other symptoms include:
- frequent or recurrent vomiting via the mouth or nose
- poor feeding, unlatching often and body arching
- choking or gagging during feeding
- crying during feeding
- recurrent chest infections and cough
- poor weight gain
- poor sleep patterns such as catnapping during the day and frequent night waking (though some will sleep well at night).

139

The Silent Reflux Baby

A silent reflux baby is difficult to detect as there are no obvious symptoms. For this reason it often goes undiagnosed or misdiagnosed. Undigested milk rises, burning your baby's oesophagus, then descends again into the stomach, undetected.

Telltale signs to watch for include frequent ear and sinus infections, chronic hoarse vocal sounds (often accompanied by an inflamed throat without infection), gagging or choking and poor sleep habits, often with frequent waking.

Colic

Colic is the medical term for frequent crying in a young baby who appears to be otherwise healthy and well fed. It is a common yet poorly understood condition, affecting up to one in five babies.

Colic is typically associated with prolonged and inconsolable bouts of crying, often occurring in the late afternoon or evening and lasting several hours. Babies suffering from colic often clench their fists, curl into the fetal position or arch their backs.

Experts tend to disagree on what causes colic, although it is commonly associated with a build-up of intestinal gas in a baby who has not been burped properly. I also believe stress to be a major factor.

There is no clear evidence that colic has any long-term effects on a baby's health.

What is the Difference between Reflux and Colic?

The similarities between colic and reflux make it difficult to tell them apart. A decade ago, colic was an across-the-board diagnosis given for any unexplained symptom of an unsettled baby with feeding or sleeping issues. These days we tend to talk more about reflux, although colic still exists.

In my experience, reflux symptoms occur in the upper digestive tract — the esophagus and stomach — whereas colic tends to affect the lower digestive tract — the small and large intestines. How to tell the difference? It's difficult; a lot of babies suffer from both.

Babies with reflux and colic tend to be excessively irritable, cry inconsolably and have difficulty feeding and sleeping. In my experience, there is no such thing as a fussy baby. These babies are trying to tell you something and it is important that you seek professional help until you have a more contented baby.

How to Nurture a Colicky or Reflux Baby

Experts tend to disagree on how to treat reflux and colic. Some professionals believe that food intolerances are a contributing factor while others sweep it under the carpet.

Having witnessed approaches from a variety of professional people around the world over several decades, here are the strategies I have found to be useful. They do not always eliminate colic and reflux fully, but they help relieve pain and discomfort and make life easier for all.

It is important to keep in mind that babies with reflux and colic need extra nurturing to help them through this distressing phase. Luckily, babies tend to grow out of reflux and colic.

During Feeding
- Ensure that you are feeding for hunger and not comfort.
- Make sure your baby is productively sucking and swallowing during feeding.
- Avoid snacking and catnapping — your baby's digestive system needs time to digest before feeding again.

If breastfeeding:
- practise a deep latch-on technique (see page 111).
- once attached to the breast, lower your baby's bottom so they are feeding with their head slightly elevated
- make changes to your diet by eliminating one of the following food groups — dairy, sugar, wheat/gluten — for a minimum of 72 hours. If after doing this your baby's symptoms have not improved, it's likely that the cause is other than intolerances to any of these food groups.

Breastfeeding and Dietary Changes
In my experience, food intolerances can often contribute to reflux and colic. By identifying and removing the food that is causing it, your baby will be much happier.

141

It is not necessary to eliminate all the food groups at once, as your aim is to detect which one is causing the intolerance. It is best to do it one at a time.

Doing so requires reading all labels and removing the food group 100 per cent for a minimum of 72 hours. (You can't sniff it or have so much as a pin-head.)

More often than not, one food group will produce results.

Try the following:
- Eliminate all dairy products for a minimum of 72 hours.
- If there is no change, reintroduce dairy and eliminate foods with gluten/wheat.
- If still there is no change, reintroduce gluten/wheat and eliminate foods containing sugar.

If bottle-feeding:
- feed in a calm and quiet environment

- make sure your baby is comfortable during feeding
- position your baby in a more stretched out position during feeding so that their stomach area is not compressed or restricted in any way
- check the teat size provides the right flow for your baby
- try a lactose-free formula
- try a partially hydrolysed or hydrolysed formula
- when making up formula do not shake but swirl.

Some experts recommend that reflux and colicky babies be kept upright for some time after feeding, however this is not always practical, especially if it encroaches on sleep time or, for older babies, valuable floor time. In my opinion, reflux and colicky babies need all the sleep they can get and an overtired baby is much more difficult to settle. Using my engulf hold will allow your baby to be upright and have their nap at the same time.

Other Options
- Raising the head of your baby's bassinet/cot and change table sometimes helps with colic and reflux.
- If raising a bassinet or cot for your reflux or colic baby, check out the Safe T Sleep Sleepwrap — a useful product that keeps your baby safe and in one position, and which can be used over any sleepwear. The Safe T Sleep wrap can be used in the bassinet, cot, travel cot and on many different bed sizes.[9]
- Avoid sitting your baby upright for long periods of time — including long car journeys in a car seat — as it can put pressure on your baby's tummy and cause added discomfort.
- Avoid rocking and jiggling — babies suffering from reflux and colic dislike excessive movement.

In my experience, colicky babies respond best to being held calmly and securely in your arms, with movement, noise and distractions kept to a minimum. This may not be easy in a busy home but do the best you can.

Dummies/Pacifiers
Dummies/pacifiers are a godsend for reflux babies, providing the extra comfort they need. My motto is: *the less crying, the better.* Research shows that sucking

a dummy/pacifier increases saliva that is alkaline, which can help neutralise some of the stomach acid that rises.

Complementary Therapies and Babies

Babies respond well to complementary therapies and remedies, possibly because their systems are so receptive. The best way to find an experienced therapist is through word-of-mouth recommendation.

- Complementary remedies — colic and reflux homeopathy and herbal preparations for babies can help. Probiotics are recommended for breastfeeding mothers and baby probiotics can also be given to bottle-fed babies. Look for one that helps with cramping and bloating.
- Cranial sacral osteopathy — cranio-sacral therapy is a gentle, non-invasive treatment for babies that can produce good results in three sessions.
- Acupuncture for babies is becoming more popular as it is known to produce amazing results.

Dealing with reflux or colic is taxing on everyone involved. These tips will help you get through it:

- Remind yourself that it will pass.
- Keep as calm as possible.
- Take any opportunity to rest.
- Keep life uncomplicated.
- It may help to talk to other parents who have been through it.
- Accept help whenever it is offered.

143

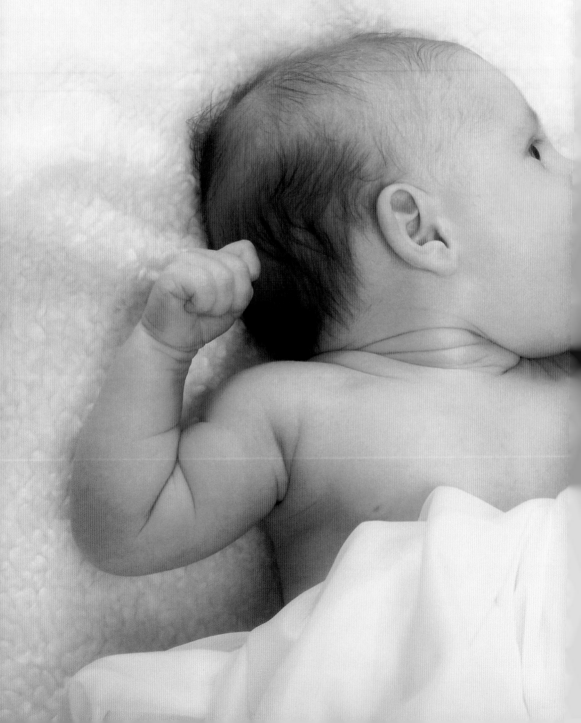

PART FOUR
Multiples

Twins

Yes, it is double the work, but it is also double the fun and twice the love ...

Over the years I have been very lucky to be able to share this incredible journey with many parents and their twins. In my experience, no one can totally prepare you for your journey as parents of multiples, but here are some suggestions that will hopefully give you a head start.

Firstly, I highly recommend creating a good network of support around you — your 'village' is essential.

Start by researching what services are available in your local community. Some communities have support groups specifically for parents of multiples, and many parents find it useful and interesting to talk to other parents of multiples to share experiences.

The Neonatal Intensive Care Unit (NICU)

It can be daunting as a parent to be part of the NICU experience, but the nurses there are 'angels' and are there to support and guide you through your first days or weeks. Be sure to ask as many questions as you wish and speak up when you don't understand something. NICU staff are more than happy to take the time to answer you.

While your babies are in NICU, involve yourself as much as possible in the care of your babies — touch is so important and helps you all significantly at this special time.

It is likely that you and your partner will be on an emotional rollercoaster, and exhausted — take a moment to stand still and cuddle each other.

As much as possible, call your babies by their names and encourage those around you to do so too — this is important as it is easy to feel a little down when people refer to your babies collectively without using their individual names.

One of the hardest issues to deal with is when you have to leave your precious little ones behind in the NICU and go home every night. It's tough.

Some parents have the added responsibility of other children at home and find dividing time between the hospital and home a challenge.

This is the time to gather your village around you and ask for help — you can't do it on your own and you are not expected to.

When it comes time to leave your amazing hospital village to go home, the real journey begins.

If, when you are discharged from hospital, you are not given a monitor, I would recommend that you buy one that combines sound, vision and movement. It will be a huge help.

It is likely that your babies will be different sizes, feed differently and settle differently. Remember, they are individuals — while one might be behaving perfectly compared to the other, believe me, this can all change.

Feeding Twins

How you feed is up to you. Some parents of twins like to tandem feed, other prefer to feed individually, and some choose to prop-feed with bottles.

Experiment and see what works best for you and your babies.

If they wake at the same time, it's a good idea to begin the feed by tandem feeding, then, after burping, to feed individually. This gives each baby some one-to-one time. The most common comment I hear from mothers of multiples is that they feel a lack of special one-on-one time with each baby.

Alternatively, you may wish to place one baby on the floor or next to you while you feed the other, then swap them over. I tend to place the baby I have just fed on the floor on their tummy so that they can burp themselves while the other baby is feeding.

Burp and change nappies, then, if needed, resume feeding the fussier baby while the other baby plays on the floor. Then switch over.

Once they have both finished feeding and it's time to return them to bed, I swaddle them and place them in their cots. You can put them either vertically or horizontally in the cot, although I prefer horizontally as it gives them more space.

Night-time Feeds

While feeding both babies at the same time during the day can work well, night-feeding sometimes requires some juggling.

Some prefer to feed the babies individually when they wake, while others choose to feed when one wakes and then wake the second baby so they can feed simultaneously. Choose what suits you best.

Once your babies regain their birth weight, and provided there are no medical reasons for waking them up, I tend to do night feeds when they wake naturally.

Perhaps the hardest part of having twins — and until you have them it is difficult to visualise — is having no time to do anything. The first few months fly by, with the time taken up by feeding and sleeping.

What You Need

Before you go out purchasing products, do your research as you will be amazed by how many businesses offer deals for multiples.

Try not to overbuy. As a guide, you will need two car seats (brand new or hired) and a double stroller. If possible, a good tip is to have a double stroller and at least one single, to give you options and a bit more freedom. For example, you could have one baby in the stroller and carry the other in a front pack, or let your partner use the single stroller while you use the front, or vice versa.

Bassinets

Buying two bassinets is an option but not a necessity. For some families it is an expense they can do without, especially as it is more than okay for your babies to share a cot while they are still small. If you are purchasing second-hand equipment, or borrowing from friends, it's a good idea to buy new mattresses.

Cots

In the early weeks one cot is enough, but you probably will find you need that second cot before too long.

Change Tables

149

A change table is not essential. However, if purchasing one, choose a larger table so that two babies can fit side by side on it while they are small.

If you choose not to buy one, I suggest you have a designated area that can be used in place of a change table — either on the floor or on a spare bed. For safety reasons, many parents choose the floor as a safer option.

Feeding Essentials

A feeding pillow especially for twins, along with a very comfortable feeding chair.

Nappies

You will go through approximately 140 to 200 nappies a week — this equates to 10 to 14 nappies a day.

Cloth versus disposable? If you are unsure, try them both to see which you prefer.

Baby Wipes
There are several on the market. Try the different brands to see what works for you.

Nappy Sacks
These are great for disposing those smelly nappies in.

Clothing ... How Much is Too Much?
Here is a basic list of clothes and bedding you may need for two babies:
- 12 bodysuits (onesies, singlets with snaps)
- 12 Babygros or outer clothes — keep them simple and easy to use
- 14 swaddles
- 24 burp cloths (old-fashioned flat nappies) — these have many uses
- 12 bibs (I tend to use those with snaps, as Velcro scratches and catches longer hair)
- 6 fitted crib sheets (more if not sharing the same cot)
- 4 covers for changing mat (optional) — I tend to recommend disposables to reduce laundry.
- 4 hats — depending on climate
- 4 sets of booties.

How many items of outer clothing you need, such as cardigans, depends on the season you give birth.

Hygiene
To keep yourself and your babies healthy, have a bottle of hand sanitiser for visitors to use, and for when you come in the front door. Around the house, it is your choice as to whether you choose to wash your hands or use hand sanitiser — most do a mix of both.

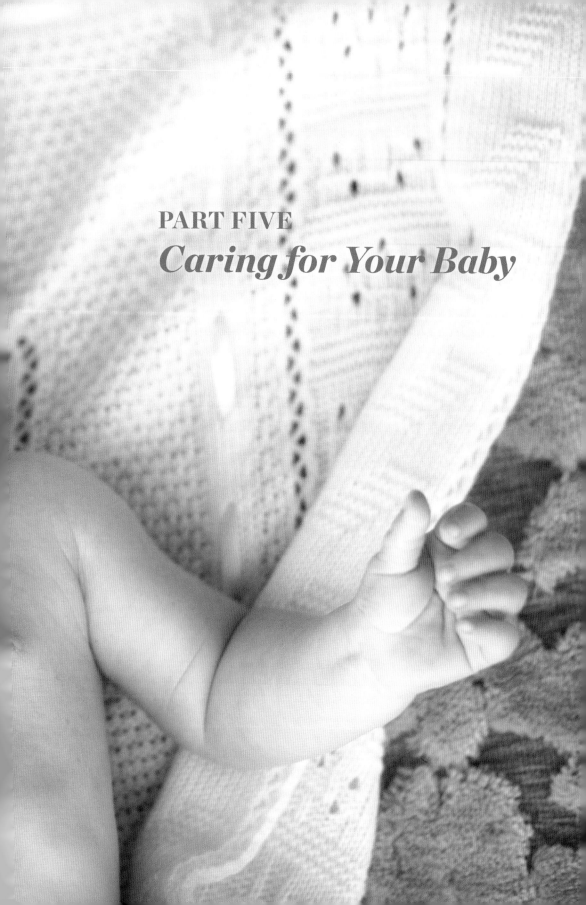

PART FIVE

Caring for Your Baby

The Hands-on Stuff

Jaundice

Neonatal (infant) jaundice is common in newborns, especially in the first few weeks following birth.

Jaundice indicates an excess of bilirubin in your baby's blood. Bilirubin is the yellow substance produced when red blood cells are broken down by the liver. In newborns, bilirubin levels often accumulate faster than what the liver is able to pass from the body. However, by the time your baby is about two weeks old the liver becomes more effective at processing bilirubin, and jaundice usually corrects itself.

Symptoms of neonatal jaundice can include:

- yellowing of the skin
- yellowing of the whites of the eyes
- yellowing of the palms of the hands and soles of the feet
- dark, yellow urine
- pale-coloured bowel motions
- appearing listless or difficult to wake
- high-pitched crying
- high temperatures.

Yellowing of the skin usually appears on a baby's face first before spreading downwards to the chest, stomach, arms and, finally, the legs. Yellowing of the whites of the eyes is also common.

Changes in skin colour may be difficult to detect in babies with a darker skin tone. In these cases, check the whites of the eyes, the soles of the feet, the palms of the hands and inside the mouth for signs of yellowing.

Typically, bilirubin levels peak between days three and seven following birth.

Newborns are routinely examined for signs of jaundice within 72 hours of birth; however, if your baby develops signs of jaundice after this time, seek medical advice. While jaundice is not usually a cause for concern, it is important to determine whether your baby requires treatment.

In premature babies, who are more prone to jaundice, it can take five to seven days to appear and may take a month or two to clear.

Treatment

If your baby shows signs of jaundice, your doctor will first need to measure the levels of bilirubin in your baby's blood to determine whether they need treatment. This is done by taking a small amount of blood, often by pricking the heel. In some cases, a urine test may be taken.

In some cases, jaundice requires phototherapy treatment to help clear it up, which involves placing your baby under blue lights. Your baby will be required to wear eye patches and be naked apart from a nappy.

Nappy Changing

- Ideally have a place set aside for changing nappies. If your home is on two levels, it can be useful to have a station on each level.
- Keep products in a basket or container for easy access.
- Some parents find it easy to use the floor to change a nappy.

Change Table

My favourite change table comprises a chest of three drawers with a change table on top to store essentials as follows:

- nappy creams
- bibs, burp cloths
- hair brush, scissors, thermometer, cotton buds.

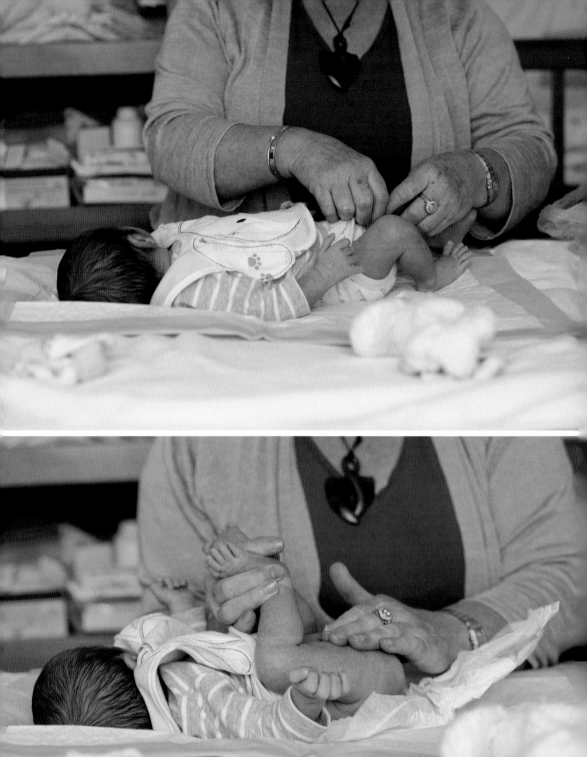

One option is to use disposable change mats to protect the surface. Alternatively, you may prefer a washable fabric cover or cloth.

Some parents prefer to use the floor instead of a change table as they feel it is safer — work out what is best for you.

Positioning

I tend to change a nappy while standing to the side of the baby. I believe this way is more nurturing, providing close eye contact and, as your baby grows, you are less likely to be kicked.

What You Will Need:
- change table or change mat
- nappies — either disposable or cloth
- bin — for disposable nappies
- bucket — for cloth nappies
- nappy sacks (good for soiled nappies)
- large cotton squares, or dry wipes
- tissues, dry wipes or cloths to pat-dry bottoms
- nappy creams
- flask or small bowl for water.

Changing a Nappy Step-by-step:
- *Never* leave a baby unattended on a high surface, even for a few seconds. Babies can roll off quite easily.
- Have all items at arm's reach: nappy (either cloth or disposable), nappy sack (for soiled nappy and wipes), wipes or water, change of clothes, creams for bottom.
- Place your baby on the change mat. If using a change table or higher surface, ensure that your body is close up to the counter top — no gap — and don't move away or take your eyes off your baby. If leaning away to dispose of soiled nappy and cloths, place one hand on your baby's tummy before doing so.
- Undo your baby's nappy and, if using disposable, turn the tapes down so that they don't stick to your baby's skin. Pull down the front part of the nappy but don't remove it fully. Instead, tuck the front flap under your baby's bottom so that the dirty nappy is closed.

- Wet a dry wipe in a bowl of warm water (use a fresh wipe each for each movement — no soiled wipes should be re-wet).
- Starting on one side, gently wash from your baby's groin area working from front to back — *do not rub as this can cause the skin to become red and sore.*
- Repeat on the other side — one wipe per side.
- Wash through the centre, then finally the cheeks and anus area.
- Using dry wipes, tissues or a cloth, pat dry (do not rub) your baby's bottom (being sure to dry in the creases) in the same order that you washed.
- Place the soiled wipes into the dirty nappy area, or into a nappy sack or straight into the bin.
- Open a new nappy.
- Gently raise your baby's bottom to remove the dirty nappy — an easy way to do it is by holding your baby's ankles so you can lift their bottom up — and replace with a new nappy.
- Release your baby down onto the new nappy.
- Apply nappy cream (optional).
- Roll up the dirty nappy and fasten it with the tabs ready for disposal. If it is a soiled nappy, one option is to place it in a perfumed nappy sack before disposing of it (using perfumed sacks helps reduce the odour of the nappy bin). If it is not soiled, throw it in the bin or, if using cloth nappies, into your nappy bin and dispose of the liners appropriately.
- If using cloth nappies, follow the manufacturer's instructions for care.
- For boy babies, ensure their penis is facing downwards to avoid them peeing upwards and getting their clothes wet.
- To fasten a disposable nappy, attach the tabs to the nappy, making sure the adhesive part is not touching your baby's skin but is fully attached to the nappy.
- Do this on both sides. Ensure the nappy is not too loose, and make sure the ruffle around the leg opening is facing outwards to prevent leakage (if the design calls for this).
- Some disposable nappies come with a notch cut out to accommodate the umbilical cord. Alternatively, you can fold the nappy down so that the cord isn't covered.
- Wash your hands or use a hand sanitiser.

158

How Often Will Babies Go between Bowel Motions?

Some babies have bowel motions at each feed, however, babies can go up to 10 days without pooing once breastfeeding is established. This is okay as long as they are content, weeing and putting on weight.

Skincare

A newborn baby's skin can be sensitive.

- Choose the most natural products and avoid scented skin products. If you choose to use products, choose the most natural.
- When bathing, don't leave your baby soaking in the water as it can dry out the skin.
- Pat dry rather than rubbing and be sure to dry in the creases under the front of the neck, behind the ears and knees.

Dealing with Meconium

After washing your baby's bottom, pat dry (avoid rubbing the skin), ensuring you get into all the creases. Once the skin is dry, apply Vaseline to stop meconium sticking to the skin.

Thrush

Oral thrush is caused by a yeast fungus called *Candida albicans*. It is common in babies and is usually harmless and easily treatable. If you think your baby may have thrush:

- it is likely your baby may not be feeding well
- check inside their mouth *before feeding* as there may be white spots or patches on the tongue or the inside of their cheeks — these look like milk curd but usually cannot be rubbed off easily
- if breastfeeding, your nipples may be itchy, red or inflamed
- seek treatment from your doctor for both you and your baby.

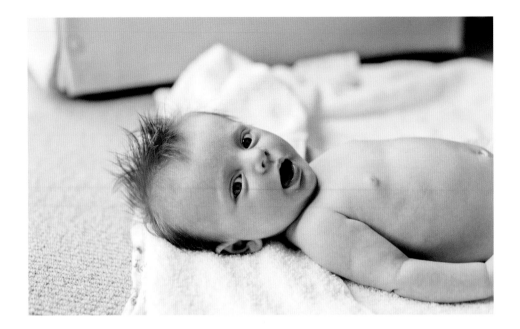

Bathing a Baby

Bathing a baby takes a couple of minutes — in fact, it takes longer to undress, dry and dress a baby than it does to bath a baby. Staying in the water for longer periods can dry out their delicate skin and cause irritation.

More time will be spent in the bath when they are toddlers and can enjoy playing in the bath.

Change Table or Floor

Before bathing, lay a towel on the change table or floor and set up so that everything is ready. Arrange the clothes in order of dressing so at the bottom of the pile are the outer clothes and on top are the under layers.

160

Running the Water

Keep the water shallow so it is more manageable (however, some babies like a deeper bath — it's your choice). Five to eight centimetres (two to three inches) will be sufficient until you and your baby get used to it. Your baby doesn't need to be fully submerged, however some babies prefer this. Find your comfort zone.

Water temperature should not be scalding or too cool. A good range is 36–38°C (97–100°F). Let your baby guide you — some like it warmer than others.

Keep in mind that in a large bath, shallow water can turn cold very quickly. If both hot and cold water come through the same tap, run the hot water first then balance the temperature by adding cold water.

Mix the water well with your hand, then test with your elbow for a better indication of its temperature. Hands tend to be more desensitised to temperatures.

You may wish to add olive oil at this point as it helps prevent dry skin. Drizzle it into the water as you would dress a salad. (Be aware this can make handling your baby slippery.)

Have ready the liquid soap, baby shampoo, a sponge or cloth, an extra cloth or two, and two to four cotton pads for washing your baby's face and eyes. Remember, babies don't *need* bath products — it's a personal choice.

Place the bath mat on the floor.

Pre-bath

It's a good idea to place your baby on a towel on the floor next to you as you run the bath. They are then free to kick and flail their arms. If it is hot weather, you may have already undressed your baby or, if it is cool, keep your baby dressed until ready to place into the bath.

- Clean your baby's face and eyes before placing into the bath.
- Wet two cotton pads under the running water and gently wipe your baby's eyes, using a fresh cotton pad for each eye. Wipe from the inner eye to the outer eye.
- With a cotton pad wipe from the centre of your baby's forehead down and around the sides of the face, chin and across the nose area.
- Then dry the eyes and face gently with the bath towel in the same order.

161

Into the Bath

- Lift your baby in your arms, again with the head resting in the wrist area and the body supported by your forearm, and your other hand supporting the buttocks.
- Using a scoop motion, slide your non-dominant arm under the baby's neck and shoulder region so that the baby's head is resting on your wrist/lower forearm and the other hand slides under their lower body, supporting the buttocks. (The reason for having your hand under their buttocks is that when you are lowering the baby into the water, your hands hits the water first — another precaution in case the water is not the right temperature.)
- If your baby cries in the bath, try laying a wet cloth over the tummy.
- Using a sponge or cloth, wet hair and scalp thoroughly. Squirting a small amount of shampoo into your hand (do not apply directly from the bottle to your baby's head), lightly massage the scalp, especially the fontanelle.
- Remember that you are also washing the scalp, not just the hair.
- Rinse well using a sponge or cloth, focusing on both the scalp as well as the hair.
- Wash under the neck area, the armpits and the bottom with a little natural soap (optional), then rinse off.
- If the water is shallow, turn your baby over onto their tummy, being sure to support their chin by cupping it in your hand, to wash the buttock crease (this is not recommended in a deep bath) then turn them back onto their back.
- Remove your baby from the bath and place on a towel.

162

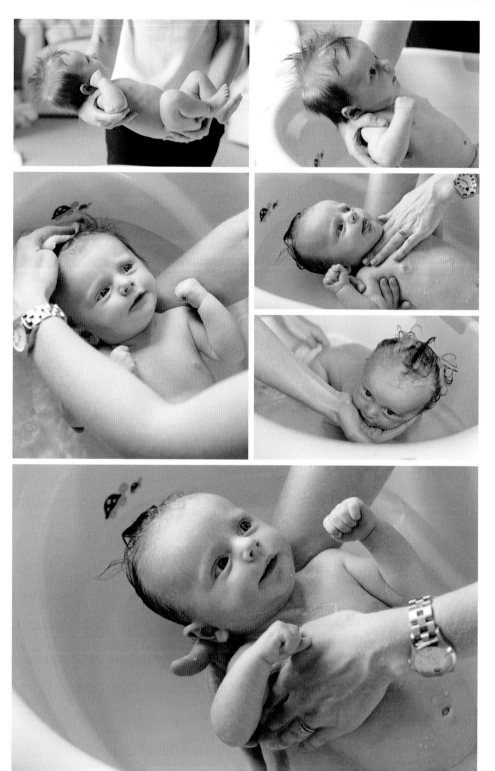

Drying

- Re-dry face, if wet.
- Towel-dry the hair, giving the scalp a gentle but firm rub, especially over the fontanelle. Then dry (pat, not rub) the neck, behind the ears, folding the ear towards you to dry between the scalp and ear.
- Place your baby's chin in the palm of your hand and raise the head backwards slightly so you are able to properly dry the neck creases in the front by patting dry with the towel.
- Raise the arms to pat dry between the inner creases.
- Turn your baby over onto their tummy to dry the back of the neck, buttock crease and the back of the knee creases.
- When drying the bottom area, be sure to get into the groin creases and under the genitals.
- When drying the body, *do not rub*. Your baby's skin is very sensitive and doesn't need exfoliation.
- Turn your baby onto their back again and dry the palms, checking between their toes and fingers for fluff. I think it is comforting to keep talking to your baby during this process, telling them what is happening and what you are doing next.

Dressing

To avoid boy babies weeing everywhere, I tend to put their nappy on first. However, an option is to start with a bodysuit first and then the nappy.

164

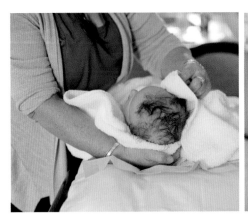
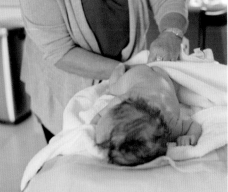

Bodysuits/Onesies
- Undo all snaps.
- Using both hands, stretch open the neck of the garment as wide as possible and bunch up the garment so it makes a hoop.
- Hook the front of the garment under your baby's chin, then lift and pass the back of the garment over the head, being careful not to drag it over your baby's face.
- Bunch up the sleeve over your hand, starting from the wrist end, and then with your free hand, feed your baby's hand up through the bunched sleeve to meet your other hand. As you take hold of your baby's hand to pull it through, be sure to enclose it in your hand to protect your baby's fingers as it passes through the length of the sleeve.
- Do the same on the other side.
- Gently raise your baby's body so you can pull the garment down the back — an easy way to do this is by holding your baby's ankles so you can lift them up.
- Fasten snaps.

Outer Garments
Babygros/sleepsuits — a garment with feet and snaps

Two ways to put on a one-piece outfit:
1. Undo all snaps and lay the outfit out on a surface. Lay your baby on top of the outfit. **165**

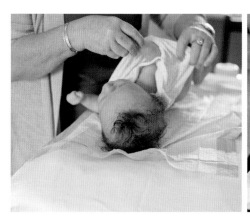 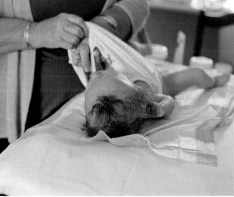

Bunch up the sleeve over your hand starting from the wrist end and then with your free hand, feed your baby's hand up through the bunched sleeve to meet your other hand. As you take hold of your baby's hand to pull it through, be sure to enclose it in your hand to protect your baby's fingers as it passes through the length of the sleeve.

Take one foot and insert it into the enclosed foot part of the garment.

Fasten the snaps — I find it easier to start at the foot and work upwards.

Repeat on other side.

2. Undo the top three or four snaps (depending on baby size).

Lay your baby on a surface.

Take the garment and bunch up a leg/foot and pull it up the leg as if putting on socks. Do the same for the other leg/foot.

Ease the rest of the garment upwards — you shouldn't need to lift your baby to do this.

Bunch up the sleeve over your hand (starting from the wrist end) and then with your free hand, feed your baby's hand up through the bunched sleeve to meet your other hand. As you take hold of your baby's hand to pull it through, be sure to enclose it in your hand to protect your baby's fingers as it passes through the length of the sleeve.

Fasten snaps.

Nightie

- Undo all snaps (if any).
- Using both hands, stretch open the neck of the garment as wide as possible and bunch it up so it makes a hoop.
- Hook the front of the garment under your baby's neck, then lift and pass the back of the garment over the head, being careful not to drag it over your baby's face.
- Bunch up the sleeve over your hand starting from the wrist end and then with your free hand, feed your baby's hand up through the bunched sleeve to meet your other hand. As you take hold of your baby's hand to pull it through, be sure to enclose it in your hand to protect your baby's fingers as it passes through the length of the sleeve.
- Do the same on the other side.

- Gently raise your baby's body so you can pull the garment down the back —
  an easy way to do this is by holding your baby's ankles so you can lift them up
  and with your free hand, pull the nightie down to straighten.
- Fasten snaps (if any).

Blocked Tear Duct or Sticky Eye

Sticky eye is a common condition in newborns and is caused by a blocked tear
duct. Tiny tear ducts drain tears from the eyes into cavities near the nose.
Sometimes these ducts do not open fully at birth or they can become blocked or
clogged later.

There is no way to prevent sticky eye and, in most cases, it corrects itself
between six and 12 months. It can be treated at home by using breast milk,
saline or boiled water.

Massage

Often when the tear duct is blocked you can feel a bump in the corner of the
eyelid near the nose. Using a cotton bud or the tip of your clean finger, massage
gently up and down or in a semi-circle from the corner of the eye inwards
towards the nose. It's good to do this regularly — I tend to do it every nappy
change or while having a cuddle.

Saline

In a sterilised container, mix half a teaspoon of salt with a cup of boiled water
and allow to cool to warm. Dip a clean cotton pad into the saline solution and
wipe from the inside of the eye outwards. Dispose of the used cotton pad and
re-wipe with a fresh pad. Do this regularly throughout the day, for example,
incorporating it into the nappy change.

Refresh the saline mix every 24–48 hours.

Breast Milk

Your breast milk contains a natural antibiotic and can be used like a saline
solution.

Cradle Cap

Cradle cap is the name given to the yellowish, greasy, scaly patches that appear

167

on the scalp of young babies. It can also affect the eyebrows, forehead and behind the ears.

It appears in the first two months and can last for some time. What causes cradle cap is not clear although some medical professionals link it to overactive sebaceous glands. Flakes build up and, left untreated, cause a cap that in some cases cause hair loss.

It is important to stimulate and keep the scalp clean by washing regularly. This will help reduce the build-up of flakes. Effective treatment involves applying Vaseline or coconut oil regularly and washing the hair every night. Use a generous amount of Vaseline and massage well into the scalp. Leave for 20 minutes, then gently massage. The flakes will start lifting. Be careful not to rub too hard.

Reapply Vaseline throughout the day and repeat the above. A good time to do this is during the nappy change.

At night, wash the hair using a gentle baby shampoo. Using a sponge or cloth, wet hair and scalp thoroughly. Use a very small amount of shampoo and lightly scrub the scalp with your fingertips, especially over the fontanelle. Be sure to squirt the shampoo into your hand and not directly onto your baby's hair or scalp. Rinse both the scalp and hair using a cloth or sponge. Firmly rub dry the hair with a soft bath towel, ensuring that you are drying the scalp too. Next brush the scalp in circular motions to lift the cradle cap.

The above treatment will not cure the worst type of cradle cap within 24 hours but it should improve it. It may take 10 days to fully get rid of it. Some cases will return days or weeks later so be watchful for signs of redness or a dry scalp.

The forehead and eyebrows can also be treated similarly to the above. Ensure you pat dry between the ear and the scalp then, *only* when the area is dry, apply Vaseline.

Do not pick the cradle cap off as this causes weeping or could lead to infection.

Another way to lift the cap is to use a soft brush, massaging the scalp in circular motions.

Nail Care

- It's a good idea to trim or file long nails to prevent babies from scratching themselves.While your baby's nails may be very soft, they can also be sharp.
- Always tend to nails in good lighting.
- Ideally, in the early weeks use an emery board to file them back, or use your

*As parents it is important to respect
that babies enjoy their own space and
do not always need toys or someone
to entertain them.*

teeth if the nails are soft and peeling.
- If using fingernail clippers or scissors, press the finger pad away from the nail and keep a firm hold of your baby's hand. Sometimes it is easier having someone else holding your baby.
- Follow the curve of your baby's fingernail. For toenails, clip straight across.
- If you accidentally nick your baby's skin, rinse under cold water and wrap a tissue or dry wipe around the wound and apply firm pressure to stop the bleeding. If the wound becomes infected, seek medical advice.
- Do not use plasters to cover wounds as they can easily come off in your baby's mouth and cause choking.

Floor-time Activities

Place a blanket or mat on the floor. Not only does this create a clean environment for your baby, the area becomes your baby's own space. As parents it is important to respect that babies enjoy their own space and do not always need toys or someone to entertain them.

Supervising from a safe distance encourages your baby to learn to appreciate their newly found independence, which is especially important as they grow and begin to feel more confident.

Try placing a mirror in front of your baby's face to encourage them to raise their head. Babies are fascinated by the 'baby in the mirror'. Likewise, a board book or musical instrument can have the same effect. Getting down on the floor with them can also be fun as they raise their head to gaze into your eyes.

Keep in mind that babies do things in their own time. As a parent or caregiver the key is to encourage, and let your baby do the rest.

Tummy Time

Placing your baby tummy-down on the floor to play is important for your baby's development. Tummy time:
- helps your baby strengthen upper back and neck muscles

169

- teaches your baby to lift and move their head from side to side
- acts a precursor to crawling
- can be useful for babies with reflux or colic — although be prepared for a little spillage
- encourages your baby to explore their immediate surroundings and see their world from a different perspective.

Some researchers say tummy time gives babies a mental boost, rather like the increased mental wellbeing that adults feel after physical exercise. Tummy time is also thought to be a positive antidote to today's practice of babies sleeping on their backs.

For those babies who don't like lying on their tummies, it's worth persisting, even for a few seconds at a time or until they show signs that they have had enough.

Over time you will find that your baby will warm to being on their tummy and eventually it will become a regular part of floor play.

In the meantime, there are several ways to include tummy time in your baby's routine without actually putting them on the floor.

Tummy time can be combined with your baby's bath time — turning them onto their stomachs while in the water — or post-bath when dressing your baby, especially if the outfit has snaps or buttons positioned on the back. It is much easier to turn your baby onto their tummy to do up the buttons than trying to do it one-handed while holding them in an upright, seated position.

Tummy-down is my favourite position for burping a baby — I tend to put them over my knees or over my shoulder. For babies who are difficult to burp, placing them tummy-down on the floor helps release trapped wind.

When to Seek Medical Help

It is recommended you contact your doctor *immediately* if your baby:
- has a weak, high-pitched, continuous cry
- seems floppy when you pick them up
- takes less than a third of their usual amount of fluids
- passes much less urine than usual
- vomits green fluid
- passes blood in their stools
- has a fever of 38°C or above
- has a bulging fontanelle (the soft spot at the top of a baby's head)
- has a fit or seizure
- turns blue, blotchy or very pale
- has a stiff neck
- has breathing problems, such as breathing quickly or grunting while breathing
- has a spotty, purple-red rash anywhere on their body (this could be a sign of meningitis).

Always follow your own instincts — if you sense something is wrong, call a doctor immediately.

PART SIX
Practical Information

Out and About

Out and About Locally

What to pack for an outing of less than four hours:

- extra T-shirt
- changing pad and disposable change mat
- 4 x nappies
- 2 x muslin cloths
- 2 x bibs
- baby wipes, or dry wipes
- travel tissues
- nappy sacks
- change of clothes
- an extra layer — cardigan
- dummies/pacifiers (optional)
- if not breastfeeding, a bottle of formula.

Daily use for Mum:

- breast pads
- sanitary pads
- large muslin cloth for covering baby if feeding
- hand sanitiser
- snack
- bottle of water.

For Airline Travel

Work out door-to-door travel time and double it. For instance, for an eight-hour journey, pack as if for 16 hours.

For long-haul flights, take two pieces of carry-on luggage for your baby: a nappy bag and a wheel-on bag containing additional supplies. Try to avoid overpacking their nappy bag.

In the wheel-on, pack supplies to replenish the nappy bag.

Pack contents in zip-lock bags, including clothing. This is much easier when going through security, helps manage leakages and makes it easier to swap clean clothing for dirty clothing.

Planes can be hot. It's important your baby doesn't overheat — 100 per cent cotton is best for breathability.

The best onesies or Babygros to travel with are those with snaps down the front for ease of taking off and on.

Burp cloths and bibs can be bulky but worth sacrificing the space for.

175

Nappy Bag (carry-on)

- nappy sacks (fold and store in zip-lock bag)
- baby wipes — ideally a packet with a lid that closes
- bottom creams — good to have a mix in case flying causes a reaction
- 10 x nappies
- 4 x disposable change mats
- saline nasal drops
- infant paracetamol and ibuprofen
- 6 x dummies/pacifiers (in a zip-lock bag)
- 4 x burp cloths
- 6 bibs (optional)

Clothing for Carry-on Bag
Pack three sets of the following in separate zip-lock bags:
- 1 x cotton undershirt
- 1 x outfit, e.g., a baby-grow (with feet) — 100 per cent cotton
- 1 x cardigan
- 1 x hat.

Additional:
- 2 x large muslin cloths
- 1 x cotton blanket for stroller/pram.

Wheel-on Bag
- hand sanitiser
- nappy sacks (ideally those that you pull through the lid)
- 1 x packet of nappies — work out quantity based on 16 nappies per 24 hours
- 2 x packets of disposal change mats
- 4 x large muslin cloths
- 2 x small cotton blankets
- 6 x burp cloths
- 6 x dummies/pacifiers
- 6 x bibs (optional)

Clothing:
- 6 x separate zip-lock bags containing the following:
- 1 x cotton undershirt
- 1 x outfit, e.g., baby-grow (with feet) — 100 per cent cotton
- 1 x cardigan
- 1 x hat.

Baby carrier/Front Pack/Sling
Optional. In my experience, it is great to have one with you, however I find the stroller more practical.

On the Plane
Use one of the cotton blankets or a blanket provided to make a roof over the area where your baby will be sleeping.

Going through the Airport
Stroller — easy and gives you somewhere to hang the lighter bags (if doing this, don't let go as the buggy will tip over). Some travel strollers also allow you the option to lie your baby flat, which is fantastic for longer journeys.

Handbags
I tend not to use handbags as they get in the way. Keep a section of the baby bag designated for wallet, phone, keys, and make-up.

Returning to Work
It is a personal choice as to whether or not a mother returns to work.

It is not uncommon in today's society for mothers to contribute to the family income and, in some households, the woman is the principal income earner.

Returning to work can often create feelings of guilt yet in my experience, many women become better mothers by returning to work.

Do whatever works for you and try not to listen to other people's judgments. You're never going to please everyone. Once you know what your work commitments will be, start considering your options for childcare.

177

Childcare

Choosing the person who will stand in for you when you're not there is an important decision to get right.

Define your needs and have a clear idea of what role you want your hired help to play in your family.

If seeking qualified help, know which qualifications will best serve your needs. Although role definitions and job descriptions vary from country to country, by and large most fall into the following categories:

- post-partum care provider/baby nurse/maternity nurse
- maternity nanny
- professional nanny
- nanny
- nanny/housekeeper
- mother's help
- au pair
- babysitter.

Post-partum Care Provider/Baby Nurse/Maternity Nurse

Also known as a maternity nurse, baby nurse or mothercraft nurse, this person is a qualified nurse hired soon after the birth, on a short-term basis, primarily to educate and support you and your partner in all aspects of baby care. Key qualities to look for include good communicative skills, hygiene, being well-organised and respectful of your home and belongings.

Maternity Nanny

This person can be either a qualified nanny with newborn experience, or a person with hands-on experience and a knowledge of newborn babies (not qualified). A maternity nanny is hired soon after the birth on a short-term basis to support you and your partner in caring for your baby.

Professional Nanny

This is a nanny with qualifications and experience. This person is there to give support and take guidance from you as to how you wish to raise your child.

Nanny

A non-professional nanny is a person without qualifications who may or may not have experience. A nanny could be a mature person with 30 years' experience, or a young woman who loves children yet has no experience.

Nanny/Housekeeper

This person is unlikely to have qualifications as a nanny and will perform housekeeping duties.

Mother's Help

This person is often young, unqualified and hired to help with sundry tasks as well as to babysit.

Au Pair

Traditionally, an au pair arrives as a visitor from a foreign country and comes to formally study the culture and language. They work for a few hours a day in exchange for full board and a small wage. Nowadays, the term 'au pair' is the name loosely given to home help and differs from country to country and family to family.

Babysitter

In many countries there are legal requirements governing the age and hours of a babysitter.

What Qualities to Look For

A brilliant CV, impressive references and years of experience are a good start but, most importantly, I would ask myself the following:

- Does this person have my baby's interests at heart?
- Is this person kind and caring?
- Will they fit into my family life?
- Are they going to be nurturing to my child, whether I am there or not?
- Are they clean and tidily presented?
- Do I want them in my space — and close to my child — on a regular basis?
- Do they have initiative — would they know what to do in an emergency?
- Could this person replace me if I were incapacitated?
- Would they be tolerant of my toddler?
- Is this person inclusive, respectful of my partner, my extended family and my pets?

This is a good opportunity to listen to your instincts. More often than not, it comes down to a feeling.

Getting It Wrong

It happens! Often applicants and interviewers behave differently during interviews, or what seemed in theory to be suitable proved in reality to be impractical.

If you find you have made the wrong choice, don't be afraid to admit it. Tell the person as soon as possible that it hasn't worked out and arrange to terminate the employment. If you do not like them, it is likely your baby won't either.

Try not to fall into the trap of thinking now is not the right time to fire your help because you're busy. Do what is best for everyone involved and start again.

Trial Period and Contract

Offering a trial period and drawing up a contract is a good idea for both parties.

How to Find Help — Agencies versus Word-of-mouth

This is a personal choice. Some people prefer to use agencies in the belief that the correct checks and screening will have been done, while others prefer

181

word-of-mouth recommendations. Here are a few things to consider:

Agencies

Agencies filter applications quickly and save time and angst. A good agency can also serve as a sounding board and can guide you regarding both you and your baby's needs.

Before hiring, double-check the references and run a police check — agencies will claim to have done this but it pays to do so yourself, *before entering contracts.* It is also worth checking with ex-employers to compare the applicant's strengths and weaknesses, while bearing in mind there may be unresolved differences. In these cases, try to read between the lines and keep in mind your own needs. For example, ex-employers may in one breath be raving about their former nanny and badmouthing her in the next. This applies to recommendations as well.

Read the fine print to know your rights before committing to an agency nanny. Normally the agency is obligated to find a replacement if the trial period is not successful.

Know:
- your rights
- what the agency's fee covers
- the nanny's rights
- the length of the trial period
- the obligations of the agency.

All agencies charge a booking fee, which is usually per placement and includes a trial period.

Contracts can vary but it pays to know from the outset how long the trial period is and what your cancellation rights are, as sometimes an agency will charge again once the trial period has been fulfilled. It can happen that the nanny works the trial period then gives their notice, leaving you having to pay a further fee to the agency for a replacement.

'In my opinion, the most important skill for a maternity nurse, nanny, au pair or caregiver is to know when to be around, and when to give the parents their space.'

Word-of-mouth Recommendations

While word-of-mouth recommendations have obvious advantages, be mindful that your friends' requirements — and how they bring up their children — may not be the same as yours. Often endorsements from friends of friends work out better than those of close friends or family.

On the down side, when taking on recommendations from those close to you be aware there is a risk of offending your friends if their recommendation doesn't work out — as well as the chance of gossip going back and forth between households.

Handing Over Your Baby

Many mothers find it tough seeing another person caring for their baby. Some get jealous when they see their cherished child respond lovingly to another carer and often dislike themselves for feeling this way. This is very normal — you are a mother with protective and nurturing instincts. There will be times when you have no choice but to hand over your baby. Try to balance these times by spending as much time as you can with your baby without your child minder.

An experienced childcare person will know when to step back and give you time with your baby.

183

When you conduct your interviews for a nanny or maternity nurse, discuss your views on nurturing and how a crying baby should be comforted. Ask about qualifications and experience and don't forget to check references. It's important you both have the same expectations regarding routine, house rules, hours and remuneration.

PART SEVEN
What Do Parents Say?

Parents Speaking Plainly

Mother of Ollie
On Becoming a Mum

My journey into being a mother has taught me the importance of just stopping and being. It's taught me the importance of dropping the mask and of not trying to be Superwoman. It's taught me that there is no right way or wrong way. And, most importantly, it has taught me that there is no greater gift than being a mother.

I know it sounds clichéd but becoming a mum for the first time totally rocked my world! That first moment of looking into my little boy Ollie's eyes is a moment that will be forever etched on the depths of my soul. Suddenly, I was responsible for someone other than myself and I simply couldn't remember life without him. The fact that I had created this little person in just nine months was truly mind-blowing.

Despite the enormity of this life-transforming moment, I thought I had motherhood sorted; I thought that being a chiropractor, holistic nutritionist and women's wellness coach who sees a lot of mums, babies and mums-to-be would mean I had a head start. While it may have given me an intellectual understanding of the physiological changes that our bodies go through during pregnancy and post-birth, it also proved to be a hindrance.

I thought that because I had taken care of myself during pregnancy and had always been fit and strong, I would be immune to all those physiological changes that happen.

So often I see new mums who want to 'get back to normal' or 'get their bodies back' or 'feel some sense of normalcy again'. I had read articles and books about the 'baby moon' and the importance of the 'fourth trimester'. Heck, I even talked to my clients about it.

But despite all this, no one had actually sat down and told *me* what to expect in those few days and weeks post-birth.

That's why people like Dorothy are so very important — to help us on our journey in parenthood. Dorothy has cared for more newborns than any of us ever will!

On Day One — 'Holy ****, I'm a Mum!'

No one really talks about what it feels like after you've had a baby. There is a knowing smile or nod that occurs between mums that says 'Welcome to the club', yet no one mentions the extreme emotions or what you will feel like physically. (Why is it that we new mothers feel we need to put on a mask and present ourselves perfectly to the outside world?)

Ollie's birth couldn't have been more textbook-perfect. His birth was completely natural — he was born at home, by choice. For me, being around the comforts of home was calming.

However, I hadn't anticipated how weak, vulnerable, tender and sore I would feel afterwards — despite the post-partum bliss. I think there was a part of me that thought I would pop out the baby, put on my running shoes and go out for a walk … deluded, I know! Seeing Kate, Duchess of Cambridge walk out of the hospital in high heels and perfect hair the day after giving birth probably didn't help my post-birth expectations either.

187

On Dealing with the Post-partum Body …

Most of us new mums — especially first-time mums — are so focused on the birth we forget to think about what *we* might need to recover (and I'm not just talking about the obligatory granny panties and maxi pads here). I had done the pre-birth prep, but I had totally bypassed what I might need to recover and heal.

I can still remember sending my husband out on Day Two to collect some natural products to help my lady parts feel a little more comfortable … oh, the glamour of it all!

No matter how much your body is designed to bring a baby into the world, nor what type of birth you end up having, giving birth is a big deal and requires recovery time.

*'Tis true … motherhood really is the most rewarding,
humbling (and occasionally extremely tiring) job that
you will ever have, and the impact we can have in creating
the most nurturing environment for our babies in those
first 12 weeks of life and beyond is immense.*

Mother of Ollie

During these early weeks, all your body's systems are working incredibly hard to return to their non-pregnant state — reproductive, cardiovascular, respiratory, musculoskeletal, gastrointestinal, endocrine and nervous systems. In a nutshell, your body is doing a *lot* of work. All this on top of caring for a newborn and, more likely than not, lacking in the beauty sleep department.

Depending on your birth experience, the health of your body and how you nurture yourself after birth (which I know seems like such a strange concept when all your focus is on the newborn), it can take between six and 12 weeks for your body to heal.

If you have experienced some tearing or severe grazing, then it may take longer but, trust me, your body will recover — it really is extraordinary.

With hindsight, and having made a few mistakes along the way, I can now say with hand on heart that being extremely gentle to yourself in the first 12 weeks is *vital*.

Tammy, Mother of Daughter (3) and Son (6 Weeks)

My husband and I were married for 10 months when we decided to start our family. We fell pregnant immediately and were so excited that I never once considered *What if everything doesn't go according to plan?* We took birthing classes, bought what we needed for our little one and felt one hundred per cent prepared for her arrival. Then came the hurdles.

Firstly, I didn't get the natural water birth that I had planned. Second hurdle, breastfeeding was painful, draining and suffocating — nothing like the 'amazing' experience that everyone had led me to believe. Thirdly, because my baby was 'failing to thrive', I had to switch to formula. I felt as if I had failed at doing something that should just come naturally to a woman.

Then came my fourth hurdle: postnatal depression.

On Breastfeeding Issues

Failing at breastfeeding felt incredibly unnatural — it was as if I failed at doing something that should just come naturally to a woman. However, I now know it is not easy for a lot of women.

The worst part for me was giving my precious babies that first bottle of formula — after all their all-natural breast milk diet, it was like administering poison. If you haven't had much time to adjust to the idea of formula, it's hard to come to terms with it.

On both occasions, I burst into tears. Suddenly, I felt unneeded now that I was no longer their sole source of nutrition. I also felt that I had to justify myself to other mothers for giving my babies formula. On more than one occasion I was told, 'you didn't try hard enough!', or 'there's no known reason why a woman can't breastfeed'.

I had tried every drug, both natural and prescribed, lactation consultants, antenatal expressing of colostrum, on-demand feeding 24/7, skin-to-skin bonding, massage, pumping to increase supply ... you name it. Nothing seemed to help. My children were barely receiving a quarter of what they needed and, as a consequence, they were losing weight.

Both my children are happy and healthy. My two-and-a-half-year-old is not the overweight or sick child I was led to believe all formula kids become. Quite the opposite — she is thriving and amazing! It was this knowledge that I used as reassurance when we gave our son formula too. So, as it turns out, formula isn't the devil!

This time round I am not afraid to mix up a bottle of formula in public. (On that note, it's ironic how we get judged for feeding a baby in public — breast or bottle. Someone always has an issue with it.)

Now that our little family is complete and we are heading out of our final newborn stage, I am becoming increasingly optimistic. At times I still struggle with the idea that, although I have a natural approach to parenting, I have fed both my children formula. I now believe that as parents we must do what we need to do to ensure our children thrive.

On Postnatal Depression

Looking back at my daughter's first year of life, it feels like a black hole — a blur of emotions: mostly sadness, anxiety and anger at myself. Finally, when she was

10 months old, I did something that I should have done several months before — I sought help.

Medication didn't work for me — it made me feel mentally weak due to the fact that I was unable to deal with this without using drugs. Instead my doctor referred me to an amazing counsellor who changed my life.

However, two-and-half years on, I went through it all again with the birth of my son. This time around, though, I was prepared — and so was my husband. He knew what triggered my bouts of feeling low and his support was invaluable. He got up for night feeds so that I could sleep — aware of how badly sleep deprivation affected me — and he cheered me up when I was struggling to cope with my daughter on the occasions I found her behaviour overbearing. I am so grateful for the connection and love that he and I share — it has helped me immensely.

Having been there, I now know that getting help is not as scary or as difficult as I once thought. *Never feel like you are a burden to anyone for asking for help!*

It's not attention-seeking, nor a sign of weakness — it's a sign of love for yourself and your family.

Femke, Mother of Two
On Relationships

My husband and I have been together for 10 years and our relationship is very solid. And so you think that when a baby arrives, all will naturally fall into place. What I hadn't realised is that a baby gives you new reasons to argue.

It's weird because when a new baby arrives you need each other so much and yet you end up irritating each other so much more than pre-baby.

As a mother it is easy to get over-protective — we tend to think that our way is the best way. I had to practise 'letting go' when Dad was looking after him, for example, not to question the outfit he had put him in (not matching!) nor to comment on how he gave the bottle, nor make suggestions when he was over-stimulating our baby. I found it so difficult to bite my tongue!

On an intimacy level it's a huge adjustment when a baby arrives, first or second. You physically have to give so much to your baby that at the end of the day there is not much else to give. Not to mention the fact that you feel incredibly unsexy. Husband starts to feel left out and withdraws into his cave, which results in irritation from the wife as all she wants is support with the baby.

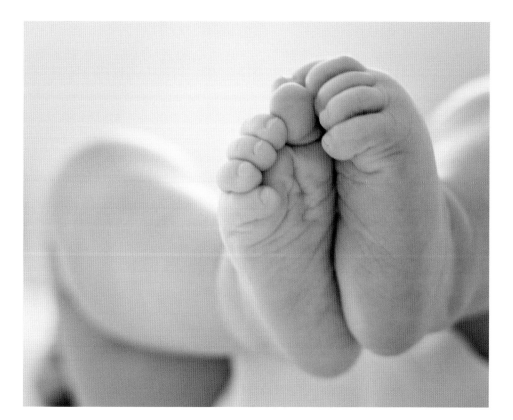

For us, this resulted in a few very grumpy weeks, followed by a huge argument before we both readjusted to the situation.

On Breastfeeding

My first experience with breastfeeding my first-born was difficult. After a ventouse delivery I was kept in hospital for one night, and very little support was given. I can clearly remember one of the nurses grabbing my breast to help us latch on in a way that felt so unnatural, as if my body had suddenly become public property. After 24 hours in hospital, my nipples were blistered and sore. At Birthcare, I received the proper help but because my nipples were already incredibly sore, I gritted my teeth every time my baby latched on.

By the time I got home three days later, our baby was unsettled and hungry. With hindsight, my milk supply had yet to establish and, in the meantime, my midwife had suggested I use a breast pump to increase supply and to supplement this with formula because he was a big baby.

Listening to my hungry baby crying was difficult, plus I felt insecure about my supply — so I pumped and pumped and pumped (even at midnight) and started giving most of his feeds, both breast milk and formula, via the bottle so that I could see how much he was getting.

Quite soon, my baby didn't want to drink from the breast any more and, because I was unable to generate enough pumped milk, I had to supplement constantly. When he was five weeks old, I went to a lactation consultant at Birthcare. I can clearly remember the meeting. When I told her what I had been doing so far, she raised her eyebrows, looked at my baby's Plunket book and asked, 'Why did you start supplementing with formula? He was putting on weight and a newborn feeding every two hours is very normal!' She went on to ask me what baby books I had been reading and, when I told her, suggested that what I was reading was not research-based and therefore I should not be reading it. Still full of pregnancy hormones, I burst into tears and at that moment felt like the worst mother on earth. Here I was trying to do the right thing, and I was made to feel as if I had been doing something really stupid.

She told me that the only way I could get my baby back on the boob was not to give him the bottle any more and to stop giving formula. Off I went and the next day — predictably — was hell. He screamed and screamed and by 4 p.m., when I couldn't handle it any more, I 'caved in'. He drank an enormous amount of formula for a little baby.

Over the next few days I did manage to get him on the breast again. Breastfeeding lasted for four months but, because he was always unsettled at the breast, I always topped him up with formula.

When my second baby arrived, I hoped I would be a lot wiser. Again, I ended up in hospital but, luckily, I remembered the technique and had a few good products with me and my nipples coped. Again, I had a big baby who was hungry, but this time I was more relaxed and able to go with the flow. There were definitely times that I doubted my supply again, based on my first experience. My husband would judge quite quickly and say 'he's hungry, your boobs are not working', to which I would respond 'how would you feel if I told you your penis was not working?'

My experience of breastfeeding is that it is time-consuming, difficult and initially painful — and the peer pressure to make it work is enormous.

Second time around I persevered and ended up enjoying it — I am so pleased I did. I wish that I had had better advice and help with my first-born as I am sure it would have been a very different experience.

I would never, ever judge any mum for giving a bottle of formula to her baby, and to those mothers who end up going down this track, please don't feel bad about it. Do what is necessary.

On Sleep Deprivation

Goodness, nobody can prepare you for this one, can they? Even though I used to read about it in magazines while I was pregnant, I would think, why can't they write about happy stuff? Only those who have gone through it truly understand it and realise that the most basic stuff in the day is an enormous effort and there is no room for anything extra, despite the fact that I seem to be home all day!

I remember my car broke down one day while I was driving and I called my husband and cried, 'My, my, my, my car, car, car broke, broke, broke down, whouaaaahhhhh!' I was sobbing my heart out on the phone. Coping competencies are non-existent and so is resilience.

Then there is the debate with your husband as to who is the most sleep-deprived. My husband used to say that he would wake up in the night too, to which I would argue back that he wasn't the one getting up and that is was a lot easier lying awake in your bed …

I have found sleep deprivation the most difficult thing of all (apart from labour). Not getting your sleep affects every aspect of your life; it's like not eating food. You need it and when you don't get it, it sucks. The dumb things you end up doing! One day I put the empty garbage bin back in its place, holding some garbage and my cell phone, then, with plenty of force, I threw my cell phone in the bin and held on to the garbage …

Unfortunately, we don't have any family around — no family member to help with the housework or take the baby for a walk so you can sleep.

The thing that kept me going was looking at my baby and feeling so utterly blessed to have him — and *not* counting the hours of sleep that I wasn't getting!

Emma, Mother of Ella (4½) and Gretta (1)

On Feeling Isolated

We were living and working in Tokyo when our first child, Ella, was born. I had an easy delivery and stayed in hospital for an entire week, as is customary in Japan, as they believe in giving the mother the best possible chance for recovery so that she is strong and able to do a good job of looking after her baby once they both return home.

193

My milk came in on the third day and, with help from the hospital midwives, breastfeeding was quickly established. However, once I left the hospital that was it — my support was pretty much over, apart from a visit from a midwife at my request, and a one-month check up with the obstetrician.

I remember feeling very alone, especially after my husband returned to work. Most of my friends also worked, so I would be at home alone all day long with my baby until friends visited in the afternoon or evenings.

I remember crying most days in the first few weeks, but I don't think it was due to PND. I felt isolated, plus I was struggling to understand what an earth I was supposed to be doing with this baby!

The most difficult part was going from having total freedom and independence and spending my time however I pleased, to having my life almost completely controlled by this tiny human! This was something I had not fully considered. Before having my daughter, Ella, I'd focused on the birth and the practical stuff like feeding, sleeping, clothing, etc., as well as what sort of parents we would like to be, without having much of an understanding on how this baby would affect our everyday lives.

On Nurturing and Self-settling

Ella was pretty much asleep for the first two weeks and I remember thinking how easy it was, wondering why people complained about it being hard. Throughout the day and night she would wake, feed, fall asleep feeding, then sleep for another three hours!

Then it became harder once she *stopped* falling asleep during feeding — and suddenly I had to come up with new ways of getting her to get to sleep, which usually involved falling asleep in my arms or in the pram.

I would take any opportunity I had to pop her into the Moses basket or cot awake, swaddled, and occasionally she would nod off, but if she so much as whimpered, I would pick her up and coax her to sleep in my arms or, alternatively, feed her until she fell asleep. Magically, when she reached the 12-week mark, she just started self-settling every time I put her in the cot, and within a few more weeks she was sleeping through the night. It was as if all the work I'd put into nurturing her in the first 12 weeks had made her feel so safe and loved that she was reassured and happy to go to sleep as soon as I put her to bed.

*It was as if all the work I'd put into nurturing her
in the first 12 weeks had made her feel so safe and loved
that she was reassured and happy to go to sleep
as soon as I put her to bed.*

Emma, mother of Ella and Gretta

On the Second-born Child

When Ella was two and a half we moved back to New Zealand and, a year later, our second daughter, Gretta, was born.

Gretta had a different entry to the world with my obstetrician deciding to induce me at 40 weeks because he said she was getting too big. Gretta weighed 4.2 kg, compared with Ella's 3.4 kg. After having a stretch and sweep, I was given an epidural before they broke my waters. I didn't feel a thing when the contractions started. Whenever I started to feel the slightest pain I topped up my epidural using the self-administering button (something I definitely did not have in Japan as most Japanese women deliver without any pain relief). Gretta was born at 7.15 p.m. and by 10.30 p.m. on a dark, cold winter's night we were leaving the hospital! I only stayed at Birthcare for one night.

Again, my milk came in quickly and feeding was easily established. But because I didn't get much rest before coming home I was utterly exhausted, and this time around it was of course much harder to rest with a preschooler around. I remember being so tired for the first few weeks, but the upside was that I was so much more relaxed as I knew what to expect.

Gretta is much easier in some ways and seems to have a much more easy-going nature. People say it is because of the mother being more relaxed the second time around, which may have something to do with it, but I also think she is just more easy-going. However, being second-born, it was impossible for me to nurture her in the same way as I had done with Ella and sleeping was an issue.

Like Ella, in the first few weeks Gretta would wake, feed and fall asleep again for three hours. As she grew, it became harder to get her to sleep. She would doze off in my arms, or during feeding, only to wake up again. Because it took so long to coax her into a deep sleep, it was almost impossible for me to help her to sleep in my arms when I had Ella to deal with as well.

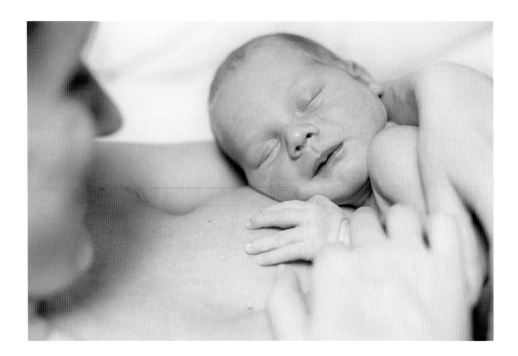

Eventually, I tried putting her in her bassinet awake and I was amazed that after a bit of grizzling she drifted off to sleep! She still tended to wake from her light sleep during the day but, if I gave her the chance, she would easily resettle.

During the evenings we were still helping her to sleep in our arms. When she woke during the night, we were so scared that she would wake Ella we would rush to pick her up as soon as she began to stir, then feed her, and rock her back to sleep.

I wonder whether the fact that Gretta was not nurtured as much as Ella contributed to her sleep difficulties, as well as the fact that I rushed to pick her up as soon as she stirred rather than giving her the chance to resettle at nights.

As it turned out, when we eventually began teaching Gretta to resettle, on Dorothy's advice, Ella was only woken by her a handful of times.

Kaya, Mother of Twin Girls
On Pumping to Exclusively Breastfed Twins

I had every intention to breastfeed my twin girls and armed myself with a feeding pillow and all the info on tandem feeding that I could find. I went into labour at 33 weeks and, after an attempt at a vaginal delivery, we ended up needing an emergency Caesarean because the girls got stuck.

Both were well, but tiny, weighing 1.7 and 1.9 kg. We spent about three weeks in NICU trying to 'fatten' them up enough to go home, which involved expressing every two to three hours, as well as trying to breastfeed.

Towards the very end of our stay, we managed to get the girls to latch on and feed so that they were able to gain enough weight in a 48-hour period to allow us to go home.

Unfortunately, the girls had picked up some bad habits and used my nipples like a straw. Although they latched on well enough, in order to fill themselves and grow satisfactorily, it meant that I ended up with cracked nipples and was in agonising pain during every feed to the point that I would be in tears before feeding began.

After a few visits to the hospital lactation consultants, the last straw for me was when my smaller twin came off my breast with a mouthful of blood from my cracked, bleeding nipple.

I had already started using a combination of pumping and breastfeeding in an effort to give my nipples a break and had decided that instead of giving up breastfeeding and switching exclusively to formula — as had been suggested to me by many people — I would pump so that I could give my girls breast milk via a bottle for as long as they wanted.

In all honesty, it's been a hell of a journey. In a sense it is the best and worst elements of breast- and bottle-feeding all rolled into one! On some days, it seems an excellent idea, on others it feels like a nightmare.

However, 10 months on, I'm proud to say our twins have not had a drop of formula and are now two bouncing healthy 9 kg babies. Plus, there are the benefits — my husband and family love the chance to share in feeding, and we are able to feed them at the same time regardless of where we are (impossible to tandem-feed twins subtly in public!). The cons, however, include feelings of guilt about not being able to breastfeed as it was something I loved doing, and the girls loved too — as well as all the cleaning and sterilising of bottles and equipment, storage and planning of transporting/heating and keeping milk safe while travelling or holidaying. Probably the worst challenge of all is finding the extra time and energy it takes to pump, especially fitting it in around two very active and busy girls.

I usually pump while they nap so that they have my attention when they are awake — which means I'm up at 5 a.m. and not in bed until just before midnight. But I know it's not forever.

On the really tough days I only need to look at my beautiful girls to see just how much good the breast milk is doing for them, regardless of the delivery system.

197

My goal now is to feed them up until a year past their due date (about 14 months in all), then to wean myself off the pump, by which time we will be ready to start on the supplies that we have diligently stashed in the freezer to get the girls through as many months as this will allow.

Mother of a Daughter (names withheld)

I first met Dorothy when my daughter was six weeks old. At the time, we were on a 7 a.m.–10 p.m. three-hourly feeding routine (or more frequently, if demanded) and feeding on demand from 10 p.m.–7 a.m. She was exclusively breastfed and had been quite small at birth, weighing 2.45 kg, so I tended to feed little and often, keeping her up for 45 minutes to an hour at a time.

On Self-settling

Prior to talking to Dorothy, I used to swaddle my daughter, hold her upright against my shoulder and then walk around the room patting her bottom until she was almost asleep. I would then try to carefully place her in her bassinet without rousing her, but she often woke and cried as soon as I put her down.

She had also just started to go from having regular, two-hour naps during the day to sleeping for 35–40 minutes at a time before waking up crying. In addition to this, she had started to display signs of silent reflux — arching her back, crying and pulling off the nipple when feeding, and audible swallowing as the milk rose up from her stomach, along with wind pain.

At first Dorothy gave me advice about self-settling — I recall that she told me that we needed to 'learn to crawl before we could walk' — so we worked on establishing 'self-settling' first before trying 'resettling'.

It had never occurred to me to put her down to sleep wide awake, but it made total sense: *if you don't allow your baby the chance to learn to settle herself, she will always need you to do it for her.*

Self-settling is not leaving her to cry it out — as soon as you have left the room and she starts to cry, then you can go back in.

At first I would leave her for up to a minute, then go back in and, eventually as she got older, we worked up to leaving her for five minutes, then going in for five, out for five, etc.

I remember it got to the stage where I would be out with my coffee group of mums and they would watch with amazement as I confidently secured my wide-awake 12-week old into her buggy and pegged a muslin over the top — and after a couple of minutes of grizzling she would be fast asleep. Then I would have to explain that, no, it's not just luck, it's actually the result of some great advice I was given by Dorothy to teach my daughter how to settle herself.

In addition to the self-settling advice, Dorothy also suggested that we let her demand-feed from 7 p.m. to 7 a.m., rather than from 10 p.m. At first I was a bit reluctant to do this — wouldn't it reduce the chance of her sleeping a big chunk of time while I was trying to sleep? But, again, Dorothy explained her reasoning and allowing my daughter to find her natural sleep rhythm during the night hours seemed to work well for her and she began to sleep from 7 p.m. to 1 a.m.

This also worked well for my partner and me as suddenly we could relax in the evenings after 7 p.m. — the last feed for the day was done! And I could go to bed early to catch up on sleep if I wanted. Gradually, over time, my daughter's six-hour chunk of sleeping time extended further and further, until at 4½ months she was sleeping through from 7 p.m. to 7 a.m. Bliss!

On Catnaps and Resettling

However, as great as the nights had become, we still had the challenge of catnaps during the day to deal with, and this was where the really hard work came in: teaching my daughter how to resettle.

At first, it was not so bad because when she would wake crying after 30–45 minutes I would go in, pick her up straightaway, sit in the comfy chair in her darkened room and, after getting her back to sleep in my arms through engulfing, cupping and shushing, would let her sleep on me for the rest of her nap while I read a book or played a game on my phone. So apart from not being able to get a lot done with my day and spending a lot of time in the dark, it wasn't so bad. In fact, it was really nice to get to cuddle my baby and to see how comforted she was in my arms. This was another great gift that Dorothy gave me — the affirmation that you are not spoiling your baby by letting them sleep in your arms, you are actually helping them to feel secure, loved and nurtured.

On Resettling in the Cot

As my daughter got older, the next step was to teach her how to resettle in the cot rather than in our arms — and that's when resettling became difficult. Gone were the days of sitting back in the comfy chair. Now it was the arm- and backbreaking work of bending over the cot in a dark room, sometimes for up to 40 minutes, cupping and shushing a grizzly infant who was so tired and struggling to find her sleep, and with the added irritation of silent reflux. I can remember how tempting it was to get my daughter up when she woke after only 30–45 minutes, but I knew that she was not hungry, was still tired and, as a reflux baby, needed at least 90 minutes to digest before her next feed.

It was a tough time emotionally and at times I felt we were getting nowhere. It seemed I could spend the rest of my life trapped in that dark bedroom with my daughter — and even then she might never learn how to resettle without my help. However, these times would coincide with Dorothy emailing me, asking me how it was all going and, when I explained how I was feeling, she would remind me that resettling is *really* hard work and reassured me that I was doing a good job and that the benefits in the long run would be huge. This always gave me renewed motivation. In the end, as promised, the effort really paid off.

On Silent Reflux

Amid all of this, we were also trying to manage my daughter's silent reflux. She didn't seem to be in any pain — aside from the associated gas pain — but I was quite sure that it was a factor contributing to her resettling difficulties. Normally I am a bit suspicious of using natural remedies for medical issues as I tend to have a lot more faith in scientifically researched treatments. However, Dorothy suggested that instead of going for a drug like Omeprazole straightaway (since there was no apparent pain), I should try going a hundred per cent dairy-free and using homeopathic drops to ease the gas discomfort. She also recommended cranial osteopathy, which seemed to give our daughter some relief. Given Dorothy's extensive experience with reflux babies and the fact that her advice to date had never steered us wrong, I decided to give it a go. It took a while, but as my daughter's digestive system matured she seemed to grow out of the reflux by around six months. What's more, I was so pleased that we had made it through without having to give her any drugs that would have interfered with the natural functioning of her digestive system.

On Creating a Rhythm

Looking back now, I am so thankful that I had the good fortune to meet Dorothy and that I followed the advice she gave me — even when at times it seemed too hard, or when I was confused by having had conflicting advice from other 'expert' sources. For instance, at 12 weeks old, when my daughter was only staying up for an hour at a time, Dorothy encouraged me to extend my daughter's awake time by 15 minutes every 10 days to increase it to one and a half hours. This was contrary to what I had been told to look for in terms of reading 'tired signs', but I tried it anyway and, lo and behold, after a week or so my daughter's body clock had adjusted and she was happily staying awake for 90-minute stretches.

Dorothy assured me that having the right amount of awake time during the day, as well as teaching my daughter how to resettle herself for day naps, would help her to sleep better at night. All I can say is that the proof is in the pudding — now at 10 months old when so many of my coffee group friends are still struggling with constant night waking and 45-minute day naps, my daughter continues to sleep 12 hours at night — and I can't remember the last time that I had to go in and resettle her for a day nap. However, should a time come when my daughter stops sleeping through the night, I know that I now have the tools and the confidence to work through it, which is a wonderful gift I would wish for all new parents.

Gail, Mother of Twins, Noah and Leo (1)
On Breastfeeding and Tongue Tie
It never occurred to me that breastfeeding would be anything other than effortless. Like many mothers-to-be, I fully expected to breastfeed my boys without problem.

201

I had envisioned myself as an earth mother, casually popping my twin boys on to feed, milk flowing out of me as they satiated themselves. What could possibly go wrong? After all, it had all sounded so simple during the antenatal classes — as for tandem feeding, what a breeze!

So when the twins arrived, I was in for a huge shock.

In the hospital, every nurse — as they poked and prodded my boobs — had a slightly different way of getting my boys to latch on. One nurse said to feed one at a time. Another said to feed them together. I was told to hold them this way ... hold them that way. We just couldn't get the hang of it.

While I was getting upset and frustrated, my boys were hungry and not shy in letting me know. Lack of milk wasn't a problem — I had gallons of the stuff so I started expressing, intending to breastfeed while supplementing with the expressed breast milk.

It certainly seemed as though they were feeding, so why were they still screaming for more food and then downing a bottle of expressed milk as if they hadn't been fed for a week?

Eventually, we saw a lactation consultant and discovered that both boys had 'tongue tie,' which meant that, for them, breastfeeding was like trying to drink through a bent straw.

The more I bottle-fed my twins with expressed breast milk, the less inclined I became to revisit breastfeeding. The boys were happier and were finally getting enough to eat. The only problem was that expressing after every feed took time — and I was utterly exhausted. Add to that the bottle washing and sterilising — there was very little time for rest between feeds.

Sleep is a precious commodity with a newborn in the house — even more so with multiples. I realised that I was beginning to resent them for my lack of sleep, which made bonding difficult.

After six weeks of expressing, and with the support of my midwife, doctor, baby consultant, friends and husband, I said goodbye to the breast pump and introduced formula. It was the best decision we made and my boys have thrived ever since. Although the timing may have been coincidental, I felt myself fully bonding with them soon after.

I would have loved breastfeeding to work out but, in the end, I learned that *what is best is what works best for you.* You are not a failure if you decide to feed your babies formula, and don't let anyone tell you otherwise.

Sheryl, Mother of Two

On Feeding Breast Milk Exclusively via the Bottle

When my first was born I was under the false impression that breastfeeding would be easy and I would have no problems. But it hurt — a lot! My midwife and the hospital midwives said that there was nothing wrong with his latch, that I should carry on and that it would come right and I would get used to it. It didn't, and I didn't.

It continued to hurt and brought tears to my eyes each time I fed. I would often cut the feed short or put off starting to feed him in the first place because of the pain. I tried nipple shields and creams, which helped a little, but after a month of this, and finding out that my baby hadn't put on any weight in a week, I gave up feeding from the breast and started pumping full time so I could feed him by bottle. Unfortunately, it was a bit late as my supply had dropped off and I had to start supplementing with formula. By three months old he was predominately formula-fed.

With my second baby, by Day Three the pain and tears had started again. My partner could see what was happening and suggested I get the breast pump out — he didn't want to see me go through it all again. So I did. It worked brilliantly and didn't take any extra time than feeding from the breast (my children were both slow feeders and I could sit for an hour at a time). I had an abundance of milk, often freezing some each day.

After a week or two of pumping, I was put under pressure (by my midwife) to try putting my daughter back on the breast. I tried and she fell asleep after two minutes. So that was it — I decided to continue to pump and, in doing so, I was able to fully feed my daughter breast milk until she was six months old.

My advice is that if it really hurts, don't be afraid to get out the breast pump.

Anna, Mother of Three
On Resettling
As with all the testimonials you will read about Dorothy, I, too, cannot thank her enough for the help (and sanity) she has given me, and my family. As a mother of three I did not think I would need any help ... how wrong was I? After 12 weeks of struggling to help our son sleep, with reflux and colic, doing everything I knew from our other two children, I finally came to the realisation that I needed *help*. The resettling techniques Dorothy showed me, in my opinion, are the most valuable tools any parent can learn. She helped me put in the hard work, which has paid off with a reward that is immeasurable — a settled and happy baby who sleeps and feeds well during the day and sleeps through the night. How can you put a price on that! Thank you, thank you, thank you, Dorothy. I would highly recommend Dorothy to anyone struggling with any baby issue. My only regret was not getting her help sooner!

Parenting beyond 12 Weeks

Parents are life-long teachers, supporting and encouraging their babies through each milestone.

At around 11 weeks, it's a good idea to start thinking about which parenting approach you would like to go forward with. Much will depend on your lifestyle, work commitments and other family demands.

Are you happy to continue with an approach that is largely baby-led, fine-tuned with parental adjustments? Or perhaps a more parentally led rhythm is called for.

This is your decision and you should not be swayed by other people's choices. *It is very much bound up with timing, instinct, respect for each other and what works best in your household.*

Rest assured that your comfort and guidance throughout the first 12 weeks will have provided your baby with enough space to develop a healthy sense of confidence and contentment so that negotiating the next phase — a phase I call 'nurturing within boundaries' — should be a natural and smooth transition for all.

Transition from Swaddle to Sleeping Bag

The ideal time to transition a baby from being swaddled to sleeping in an infant sleeping bag is at around 12 weeks. This is when the startle reflex becomes a controlled movement.

Place your baby in a sleeping bag, lightly swaddle with one arm in and one arm out, eventually progressing to both arms being free.

Another option is to drape the swaddling cloth over their chest and tuck it in under the mattress. This helps slow the movement of their hands without the restriction of a swaddle.

Moving On after 12 Weeks

Having survived the first three months, you now know that parenthood is so much more than sleepless nights and dirty nappies and that babies, by just 'being babies', have an amazing ability to fill homes with immense love and joy, transforming the lives of everyone around them.

Whether this is your first journey into parenthood or not, I am confident that your love, nurturing and guidance these past 12 weeks have given your baby (or babies) a wonderful start in life. And that, in return, their unconditional love has nurtured you and given you the confidence to go forward to the next stage with an open heart and mind.

I wish you all happiness on your lifelong journey together.

Endnotes

1 Cox, J.L., Holden, J.M., and Sagovsky, R. 1987. Detection of postnatal depression: Development of the 10-item Edinburgh Postnatal Depression Scale. *British Journal of Psychiatry* 150:782–786.

2 bit.ly/1FPgzlh.

3 Matthey, S., Barnett, B., Howie. P., Kavanagh, D.J. 2003 'Diagnosing post-partum depression in mothers and fathers: Whatever happened to anxiety?' *Journal of Affective Disorders* 74:139–147.

4 Barak E. Morgan, Alan R. Horn, Nils J. Bergman. 2011 'Should Neonates Sleep Alone?' *Biological Psychiatry* 70 (9): 817 DOI.

5 Farroni, T., Massaccesi, S., Menon, E., et al. 2007 'Direct gaze modulates face recognition in young infants', *Cognition*, 102: 396–404.

6 sleepfoundation.org/sleep-topics/children-and-sleep.

7 bit.ly/1vVj3yz.

8 One to check out is Feed Baby — Tracker & Monitor. bit.ly/18GBFbF.

9 safetsleep.com.

Index

Acknowledgements

My heartfelt thanks to everyone who has supported me on my journey, from starting out as a young, green Karitane nurse back in the 1970s, to this very special place I am in today with over 40 years' experience and writing my very first book.

I feel privileged to have had so many beautiful babies in my life, and to have been welcomed into their families with open arms.

I'd like to thank my clients who have shared their stories or have agreed to let me invade their first few weeks of precious parenthood with a camera in tow. I couldn't have done it without you.

To the wonderful people who pushed me along when I doubted myself, and propped me up when I needed it. Jocelyn Mitchell, Allison Ferguson, Charlotte McAllister and Victoria McAllister, thank you.

Thanks to Jill Daamen and many co-writers, co-readers, proofreaders and sense-checkers. It is your expertise that has helped this book evolve from my random thoughts into a much more orderly structure on the page. Thank you particularly to Deb Cochrane, Ann Packer, Ruth Brown and Emma Morrison.

Thanks, too, to the team at Bateman Publishing for letting me write this book.

Finally, my love and appreciation to all of the families around the world who let me help nurture the next generation. You've made my life rich and rewarding.

Thank you.